D1598512

The Proven Path

The Proven Path

A Roadmap to Class A Success—
The Integrated Approach to
MRP II, JIT/TQC, and DRP

REVISED EDITION

Developed by:

Roger Brooks, Andrew Coldrick, Norris Edson, Walter Goddard, Bruce Harvey, Darryl Landvater, William Sandras, John Schorr, Steve Souza, Thomas Wallace

THE OLIVER WIGHT COMPANIES

Oliver Wight

Oliver Wight Limited Publications, Inc.
5 Oliver Wight Drive
Essex Junction, VT 05452

Contents

The Proven Path

Overview

When the industrial history of the twentieth century is written, 1985-1995 will be named the Decade of Integration. It was then that the industrial world learned how to make intelligent use of many different and seemingly disparate tools and techniques, to integrate them into a coherent whole for Class A competitiveness.

Implementation methods are no different; from trial and error, observation, and on-the-job learning, a common, integrated approach has emerged. That approach is the topic of this document.

Background

About 15 years ago, Oliver Wight saw the need to create a defined set of steps for implementing Manufacturing Resource Planning (MRP II) in a manner that achieved its full potential. After studying the common elements of successful MRP II implementations at numerous companies, Wight and his colleagues developed a "roadmap" for helping companies carry out the implementation process. The process, called the Proven Path,[1] has the following important aspects:

- It's based on real world experience, on careful analysis of the experience of successful companies.

- It clearly spells out the necessary steps to be taken, and the correct sequence for them.

- It defines the prerequisites and avoids the pitfalls.

- It eliminates the need to reinvent the wheel.

The Proven Path has helped people in thousands of manufacturing companies run their businesses better, far better than they could prior to their successful implementation of MRP II. Events have shown, however, that it's time for a change.

[1] For more information, see Appendix A.

Why Change The Proven Path?

As the old saying goes, "If it ain't broken, why fix it?"[2] The answer has several parts:

1. Progress continues. Very few things are carved in granite. As new tools, new techniques, and new technologies become available, it's imperative that companies use them in order to stay competitive. At the time Ollie and his associates developed the original Proven Path, MRP II was the primary tool available in North America for achieving manufacturing excellence. Today, companies are combining Just-in-Time (JIT), Total Quality Control (TQC), and Distribution Resource Planning (DRP) with MRP II. When used together, companies gain enormous competitive advantages in terms of supplying customers with the right products at the right time, at very high levels of quality, and at very low manufacturing and logistics costs. Therefore, a company that's serious about competing will find itself in a series of implementations.

[2] Companies that have already embarked on an implementation with the original Proven Path should stay the course. It's best not to switch implementation plans midstream. On the other hand, companies not yet started, and companies thinking about re-implementation, should consider the new approach.

2. Just-in-Time brings a totally new way of thinking to a manufacturing company: continuous improvement as a way of life. JIT also carries with it a different implementation approach; the best way to implement is via a series of small pieces, rather than company-wide. This approach allows for substantial early benefits, which we'll explore more fully later.

3. To gain speed, we have applied a similar small-scale approach to implementing MRP II and DRP. This results in several significant benefits: the hands-on experience acquired from the small-scale implementation later contributes to the success of the company-wide implementation; software decisions can be made quickly when only a piece of the business is involved, allowing a fast start to the implementation effort; improvements are realized during the initial phase, rather than after the tools have been installed throughout the company; and, most importantly, top management's commitment and leadership will be strengthened as measurable progress becomes evident.

   With the traditional implementation approach, the up-front investment in time and costs are considerable, while the paybacks are several months away.

4. While JIT/TQC[3], MRP II, and DRP encompass unique bodies of knowledge and techniques, becoming successful with them is dependent on the successful management of change within the organization.

   Change involves people, and hence people are the key to the successful implementation of any of these tools. Consequently, there is a great deal of commonality from one implementation to another.

To reflect these new developments, the Oliver Wight Companies have updated the Proven Path. As we analyzed our Class A clients—who were using MRP II, JIT/TQC, and DRP at an excellent level—we found common ground for improving the Proven Path.

---

[3] Just-in-Time and Total Quality Control are two sides of the same coin. Just-in-Time is the driver that forces the identification of waste, while Total Quality Control contains the set of tools to solve and eliminate the problems uncovered by Just-in-Time. Companies that adapt Total Quality Control without Just-in-Time rarely realize the complete benefits possible from TQC, and vice versa.

Much of the thrust of the Proven Path is toward quick payback—solid results visible on the plant floor, in product quality and delivery, and in the financial statements within a very short period of time. We call these approaches "Fast-Track Implementations," and will cover them in some detail later. First, however, let's take a look at the Proven Path itself.

Anatomy of The
Proven Path—MRP II

The Proven Path encompasses 16 basic steps regardless of whether you're implementing MRP II, JIT/TQC, or DRP, and whether you're using a Fast-Track approach or following a standard company-wide implementation.

Naturally, the time frame will vary from company to company depending on its size, complexity, and competitive posture.

The implementation steps are the same for a company-wide or a Fast-Track approach. Understanding and following each step with dedication leads to Class A results. The following pages explain each of the components in the Proven Path chart. This chart is contained on the inside back cover of this book in a convenient fold-out format, which allows reference to the chart while also being able to read the book.

The explanations for MRP II, Just-in-Time/Total Quality Control (JIT/TQC), and DRP are each contained in a separate section, and each includes a detailed implementation plan. This detailed implementation plan is an improved version of the Oliver Wight Detailed Implementation Plan, which has been used by thousands of companies over the last 15 years. What needs to be done is for you to tailor the plan to your company:

1. Cross off any tasks you have already completed.

2. Add any tasks that are individual to your company's implementation.

3. Replace the generalized job titles in the plan with the names of the people in your company responsible for the different tasks.

4. Add dates. The general time frame is included in the explanation of each Proven Path element. It's up to you to develop the start and due dates for each element as well as the tasks within each element.

Appendix B is a sample of what a tailored implementation plan would look like.

Many companies today are simultaneously implementing several of these management tools, or overlapping the implementations. For example, a company may be implementing DRP and MRP II. The Proven Path approach makes it easy to integrate these implementations because the implementation approach is the same for all. To illustrate this, let's look at combining the detailed implementation plans for MRP II and JIT/TQC. This would involve the following:

1. Combine similar implementation tasks. Rather than writing a vision statement for MRP II alone, write one for MRP II and JIT/TQC. Rather than setting performance goals for MRP II alone, set them for both MRP II and JIT/TQC.

2. List separately those implementation tasks that do not overlap. For example, there would be an implementation task for the JIT Breakthrough Pilot and a task for the MRP II pilots (software, conference room, and live).

3. Modify the tasks in situations where simultaneous or overlapping implementations alter the tasks. One example of this is in the area of inventory record accuracy: some provision will have to be made for JIT/TQC point-of-use storage, which might not be the case for an MRP II-only implementation. These tasks are clearly identified in the comments sections of the detailed implementation plans.

The same approach would be used to combine DRP and MRP II, or any other combination of these implementations.

There are a number of abbreviations used in the RESPONSIBLE column of the detailed implementation plans. The table below shows these abbreviations and their meaning:

Dept.	Department
Distr.	Distribution
Engr.	Engineering (either Design or Manufacturing)
Exec.	Executive
Mgmt.	Management
Mgr.	Manager
MIS	Management Information Systems
P&IC	Production & Inventory Control
Suprvsn.	Supervision

1. Audit/Assessment I (MRP II)

Definition: An analysis of the company's current situation, problems, opportunities, strategies, etc. The analysis will serve as the basis for putting together an action plan.

Purpose: To determine which tools are specifically needed, and in what order they should be implemented. For example, a company may believe that it needs a new MRP II system. This may be true, but the analysis may reveal that because of substantial inventories in the field, implementing a DRP system first will provide the greatest payback. Once DRP is up and running, the company can focus on the incremental gain from a new MRP II system.

This step and its companion, audit/assessment II, are critically important to ensure that the improvement initiatives to be pursued by the company match its true needs; that they will generate competitive advantages in the short run; and that they will be consistent with the company's long-term strategy.

Who & How: Participants in this step include the executives, a wide range of operating managers, and, in virtually all cases, outside consultants with Class A credentials in MRP II, JIT/TQC, and/or DRP.

The process is one of fact finding, identifying areas of consensus and disagreement, and matching the company's current status and strategies with the tools it has available for execution. The end result will be the development of an action plan to move the company onto a path of continuous improvement.

TIME FRAME: Several days to one month.[4] Please note: The audit/ assessment is not a prolonged, multi-month affair involving a detailed documentation of current systems. Rather, its focus and thrust is on what's NOT working well and what needs to be done to become more competitive.

---

[4] Time Frame as used in this document refers to elapsed time, not workdays of applied effort. In this specific instance, the number of workdays would typically range from two to eight.

2. FIRST-CUT EDUCATION (MRP II)

DEFINITION: Key people must learn how the approaches work as specified by audit/assessment I: what they consist of; how they operate; and what is required to implement and use them properly.

PURPOSE: To provide a basic understanding of the approach to be pursued so the group can 1) complete a cost/benefit analysis, 2) provide the leadership necessary for the implementation, and 3) understand how to manage successfully when the new tools are available.

WHO & HOW: A small group of executives and managers (perhaps a dozen people) attend a public seminar on the approach being considered.

TIME FRAME: One to four weeks.

Note: Some executives may go through first-cut education prior to audit/assessment I. Either they will not be aware of the value of this step, or may want to become familiar with MRP II, JIT/TQC, and DRP prior to the audit/assessment. The order is not important; the critical issue is to make sure that both steps are done.

3. VISION STATEMENT (MRP II)

DEFINITION: A written document that defines the desired operational environment. It answers the question: What do we want to accomplish?

PURPOSE: To provide a framework for consistent decision making, to serve as a rallying point for the whole company.

WHO & HOW: The executives and managers who participated in first-cut education, in one or several meetings, hammer out what the company will look like and what new competitive capabilities it will have after the new approach has been implemented.

TIME FRAME: One to several days.

4. COST/BENEFIT (MRP II)

DEFINITION: A written document that spells out the costs of imple-
                  mentation and the benefits of operating at a Class A
                  level.

PURPOSE: To make possible an informed decision about whether
                  to proceed with the implementation; to build a founda-
                  tion for the project; and to ensure there is buy-in and
                  commitment from management to provide the neces-
                  sary resources.

WHO & HOW: Involves the same people and often the same meetings
                  as the vision statement. The top person from each
                  functional area should be accountable for providing the
                  estimate of benefits and the eventual achievement of
                  them.

TIME FRAME: One day to one week.

5. PROJECT ORGANIZATION (MRP II)

DEFINITION: Creation of the appropriate management and operational level team(s). Generally, this consists of a steering committee of executives and a project team of key users.

PURPOSE: To assign responsibilities and allocate people resources to the project.

WHO & HOW: Initially, much the same group as above to do the job of identifying candidates. Afterwards, certain executives and managers discuss the opportunity with the candidates to gain their acceptance of the assignment.

TIME FRAME: One day to two weeks.

6. PERFORMANCE GOALS (MRP II)

DEFINITION: Agreement of what performance categories are expected to improve and what levels they are expected to reach.

PURPOSE: To identify improvements that are expected to be achieved and how they will be measured.

WHO & HOW: Essentially the same people who attended first-cut education use the knowledge gained there to set specific targets for attainment (e.g., customer delivery performance, lead time reduction, schedule compliance, cost reduction, productivity increases, inventory reductions, etc.).

TIME FRAME: One hour to one day.

Please note: In many cases it's possible for most of the activities specified in Steps 3, 4, 5, and 6 to be accomplished by the same people in the same several meetings. This is good, since there is an urgency to get started, and time is of the essence.

MRP II
Proven Path Detailed Implementation Plan

TASK	RESPONSIBLE	COMMENTS
1. AUDIT/ASSESSMENT I	Top Mgmt. Middle Mgmt.	Assess the company's current situation. In most cases, this is done with the help of an outside consultant with Class A credentials.
2. FIRST-CUT EDUCATION	Top Mgmt. Middle Mgmt.	What is MRP II, how does it work, why should a company commit to it? Top management should attend the Top Management Course, key middle managers should attend the Five-Day Course, Executive Torchbearer and Team Leader should attend Successful Implementation Class.
3. VISION STATEMENT	Top Mgmt. Middle Mgmt.	A short, concise document defining what we want to accomplish, and when it should be in place.
4. COST/BENEFIT	Top Mgmt. Middle Mgmt.	A clear listing of the costs and benefits, agreed to by the key players.
A. Prepare cost/benefit.	Top Mgmt. Middle Mgmt.	Cost/benefit analysis.
B. Commit to implementation.	Top Mgmt.	Approve the implementation. Communicate the commitment. Deliver clear, consistent messages.
5. PROJECT ORGANIZATION	Top Mgmt.	Create the appropriate management and operational teams.
A. Executive Steering Committee.	Top Mgmt.	Include designation of Executive Torchbearer. Schedule review meetings once a month.
B. Project Team.	Top Mgmt.	Team Leader should be full-time.
C. Outside counsel.	Top Mgmt.	Outside consultant with Class A experience.
D. Spin-off task groups.	Ex. Steering Committee	Identify initial groups, more may be needed later.
6. PERFORMANCE GOALS	Top Mgmt. Middle Mgmt.	Using the ABCD Checklist, agree on expected performance levels and measurements.

7. INITIAL EDUCATION (MRP II)

DEFINITION: An educational effort for all people who are involved in designing and using the new tools.

PURPOSE: To provide a basic understanding of what the company is striving to achieve, why it is important, and how it will enable them to do their jobs more effectively.

WHO & HOW: The groups(s) selected to manage the project (Step 5) must first become more knowledgeable on the approaches. This is usually accomplished through seminars and internal education sessions. These people would then lead the education of the larger group. Business discussions led by managers and supervisors, and assisted by videotapes, have proven to be a practical and effective method of accomplishing this step.

TIME FRAME: Throughout the implementation schedule.

8. THE SALES, LOGISTICS, AND MANUFACTURING PROCESSES (MRP II)

DEFINITION: Detailed statement of how the Sales/Marketing, Logistics and Manufacturing functions will perform following implementation, and the detailed project plan necessary to achieve this.

PURPOSE: To ensure that the details of the implementation will be consistent with the vision statement; to verify that the processes that will be affected by the upcoming changes will be prioritized based on those most in need of improvement; and to create the detailed schedule necessary for effective project management.

WHO & HOW: Key people who will be directly involved lay out the detailed project schedule and, where appropriate, obtain concurrence from senior management.

TIME FRAME: One week to two months.

MRP II
Proven Path Detailed Implementation Plan

TASK	RESPONSIBLE	COMMENTS
7. INITIAL EDUCATION	Team Leader	Provide the necessary understanding to all people who will be designing and using the new tools.
A. Outside education for people who will be leaders at the in-house series of business meetings, and key managers.	Team Leader	To be effective discussion leaders, these managers need exposure at either the Top Management Course or the Five-Day Course. The key managers mentioned here are people critical to the design or operation, but who have not been covered under first cut education and who are not leaders for the business meetings.
B. Outside education for people designated as in-house experts.	Team Leader	Generally, in-house experts are designated in the following areas: Manufacturing Strategy, Sales & Operations Planning, Master Production Scheduling, Material Requirements Planning, Capacity Management and Shop Scheduling, Purchasing, Inventory Record Accuracy, Bill of Material Accuracy, and Financial Integration. These in-house experts may or may not be part of the project team.
C. Project Team/Discussion Leaders video course.	Team Leader	A series of business meetings where the general principles are translated into the specifics of operation for your company. Acquire the MRP II Video Library.
D. Top Management video course.	Executive Torchbearer/ Project Leader	A series of business meetings where the top managers apply the concepts to their company.
E. Mixed Management Overview video course.	Discussion Leaders	A series of business meetings covering the overview materials, with a mixed group of managers from each of the different functional areas. The objectives are to understand the concepts, to better understand one another, and to help in team building.

MRP II
Proven Path Detailed Implementation Plan

TASK	RESPONSIBLE	COMMENTS
F. Department specific video courses.	Discussion Leaders	Series of business meetings organized by department. The objectives are to determine specifically what changes need to be made to run the business differently in these departments. Typical groups for these meetings include, but are not limited to: Production and Inventory Control, Purchasing, Manufacturing Supervision, Quality, Sales and Marketing, Engineering, Finance, Management Information Systems, Personnel, Stockroom, Group Leaders, and Direct Labor Employees.
8. SALES, LOGISTICS, AND MANUFACTURING PRO-CESSES	Top Mgmt. Middle Mgmt.	Develop a detailed statement of how these processes will operate following implementation. The Project Team/Discussion Leaders series of business meetings (Task #7C above) generally provides most of the information needed for this task. Key issues or changes should be approved by top management.

25

9. Planning and Control Processes (MRP II)

DEFINITION: Identification of all systems and processes necessary for effective planning and control, from sales & operations planning down through detailed plant, supplier, and distribution schedules.

PURPOSE: To ensure that the formal planning and control systems either in place or to be implemented are capable of generating and maintaining valid plans and schedules for:

1. Shipment of customer orders
2. Logistics
3. Manufacturing
4. Purchasing
5. Engineering
6. Finance

WHO & HOW: The people throughout the company, in marketing and sales, manufacturing, purchasing, engineering, planning, and elsewhere who will be involved in generating plans and schedules, or in executing them. They do this by using their knowledge of the present operating environment of the company with the knowledge they gained in initial education as to what is required.

TIME FRAME: One week to three months.

TASK	RESPONSIBLE	COMMENTS
9. PLANNING AND CONTROL PROCESSES		Identification of the systems necessary for effective planning and control. Some of these systems will be implemented using the pilot approach.
A. Sales & Operations Planning.	Top Mgmt.	Can be started right away. Format, policies, unit of measure, and family designations can be developed in the first few meetings and revised as needed thereafter.
B. Demand Management.	Sales Mgr.	Focus on improving the demand side of the business through: sales planning, item forecasting, eliminating or reducing detailed forecasting wherever possible by using DRP or interfacing with customer scheduling systems.
C. Master Production Scheduling.	P&IC Mgr.	Decisions on what level in the product structure to master schedule, and what items will be master scheduled. Typically started with material planning as part of the pilot.
1. Develop a master scheduling policy.	Top Mgmt. Sales & Mktg. P&IC Mfg. Suprvsn.	Should address the following: 1. Procedure for changing the master production schedule. Who can request a change, how the proposed change is investigated, and who should approve it. 2. Periodic reviews of actual production vs. the master production schedule with an emphasis on problem resolution.
D. Material Planning.	P&IC Mgr.	Begun as a pilot.
E. Capacity Planning.	P&IC Mgr. Mfg. Suprvsn.	Sometimes implementation is delayed until after master scheduling and material planning are fully implemented.

MRP II
Proven Path Detailed Implementation Plan

TASK	RESPONSIBLE	COMMENTS
F. Shop Scheduling.	P&IC Mgr. Mfg. Suprvsn.	Includes shop floor control and input output control. Some companies today are using kanban on the factory floor in place of traditional shop floor control. Other companies are using both kanban in some areas, and traditional shop floor control in other areas.
G. Supplier Scheduling & Development	Purchasing Mgr.	Typically started as a pilot with one or several suppliers.

28

10. DATA MANAGEMENT (MRP II)

DEFINITION: Attaining necessary levels of data accuracy and structure, with timely reporting.

PURPOSE: To make decisions based on current, accurate information.

WHO & HOW: Accountability for data integrity must be assigned.

Data	People
Inventory Record Accuracy	Warehouse and Stockroom Personnel
Bill of Material[5] Accuracy and Structure	Product Engineering, Research and Development, Distribution
Routings (if required)	Manufacturing/Industrial Engineering

TIME FRAME: Up to several months.

---

[5] Often called formulas, recipes, practices, etc. in process flow manufacturing. In a DRP implementation, this step would refer to the distribution bill of material (i.e., which products are stocked at which locations in the distribution network).

MRP II
Proven Path Detailed Implementation Plan

TASK	RESPONSIBLE	COMMENTS
10. DATA MANAGEMENT		These are the steps required to attain the necessary levels of data accuracy.
A. Inventory Record Accuracy.	Stockroom Mgr.	Objective is a minimum 95 percent inventory record accuracy.
1. Measure a sample as a starting point.	Stockroom Mgr.	Develop an objective assessment of the starting point. Most companies use a sample of 100 items.
2. Provide the tools for limited access and transaction recording.	Stockroom Mgr.	Includes enough stockroom people, adequate space, counting scales, and typically a fence. In the case of a simultaneous MRP II/JIT implementation, see the JIT implementation plan for the handling of point-of-use and point-of-manufacture storage. Transaction system must be simple and easy to use.
3. Implement control group cycle counting.	Stockroom Mgr.	Used to find and fix the root causes of errors.
4. Begin cycle counting all items.	Stockroom Mgr.	Done after the causes of errors have been corrected. Several approaches are commonly used: process-control cycle counting, cycle counting by ABC code, random cycle counting.
B. Bill of Material Accuracy.	Engr. Mgr. Mfg. Suprvsn.	Objective is a minimum 98 percent bill of material accuracy, and an accurate bill of material structure.
1. Measure a sample of single-level bills as a starting point.	Engr. Mgr. Mfg. Suprvsn.	Develop an objective assessment of the starting point. Most companies use a sample of 100 single-level bills.
2. Assign responsibility for bill of material accuracy.	Top Mgmt.	Working with all the different departments who are users of the bills of material.

MRP II

Proven Path Detailed Implementation Plan

TASK	RESPONSIBLE	COMMENTS
3. Verify bills of material for correct item numbers and quantity per.	Engr. Mgr. Mfg. Suprvsn.	Typically done by exception: issue to manufacturing per the bill of material and track exceptions. A cycle audit, line-by-line audit, and/or disassembly of the product can also be used where appropriate. Objective is to highlight errors and correct them as well as correcting the root causes of the errors.
4. Verify correct structure in the bills of material.	Engr. Mgr. Mfg. Suprvsn.	Typical areas of work include: 1. Representing how material moves in the factory. 2. Showing raw material on the bills of material. 3. Including modules and self-consumed assemblies where appropriate. 4. Removing unnecessary levels from the bills of material.
5. Develop and implement bill of material policies.	Engr. Mgr.	Typical policies include: 1. Engineering (or formula) change procedure. 2. Documenting new or special products. 3. Temporary material substitutions.
C. Routing Accuracy.	Mfg. Engineering Mgr.	Objective is a minimum 95 percent routing accuracy.
1. Measure 100 routings as a starting point.	Mfg. Engineering Mgr.	Develop an objective assessment of the starting point.
2. Assign responsibility for routing accuracy.	Top Mgmt.	May involve assigning areas of responsibility if these do not already exist.
3. Verify routings.	Mfg. Engr. Mgr.	Typically done by auditing work on the factory floor for: correct work center, correct operation sequence, reasonable time standard (plus or minus 10 percent).

31

MRP II
Proven Path Detailed Implementation Plan

TASK	RESPONSIBLE	COMMENTS
D. Item Data.	P&IC Mgr. Purchasing Mgr.	Have knowledgeable people verify this information.
1. Verify order policies.	P&IC Mgr. Purchasing Mgr.	Decide between fixed-order quantity and lot-for-lot. Dynamic-order quantity calculations are not recommended. Fix the obvious errors in order quantities, use remainder as is, work to reduce the order quantities.
2. Verify lead times.	P&IC Mgr. Purchasing Mgr.	Manufactured items: use simple, consistent scheduling rules, fix the obvious problems, work to reduce the lead times. Purchased items: use current lead times, work with suppliers to implement supplier scheduling to get out beyond the lead times.
3. Verify safety stock levels.	P&IC Mgr. Purchasing Mgr.	Applies to independent demand items consistent with master schedule policy. For dependent demand items, restrict to special circumstances only.

11. PROCESS IMPROVEMENT (MRP II)

DEFINITION: Continuous improvement of all processes for sales, operations, logistics, and product design.

PURPOSE: To ensure survival, growth, and prosperity as a business. This is done by changing those processes that inhibit progress and/or are incompatible with the new vision.

WHO & HOW: Initially, only those people involved with the actual implementation, but eventually everyone in the company, should participate in this step. This is done by creating within the organization a deep commitment to continuing improvement, a creative discontent with the status quo.

TIME FRAME: Never ending.

MRP II
Proven Path Detailed Implementation Plan

TASK	RESPONSIBLE	COMMENTS
11. PROCESS IMPROVEMENT		MRP II is a planning and control system. JIT/TQC is process improvement; changing the business to make it more efficient, more productive, and less costly through the elimination of waste.
		Companies need to do both: Plan and control their business, and change their processes to continuously improve them. For the detailed implementation plan in the area of process improvement, see the JIT/TQC Detailed Implementation Plan.

12. Software Selection (MRP II)

DEFINITION: Acquisition of software for planning, control, execution, analysis, and monitoring.

PURPOSE: To provide the information that supports the users in doing their jobs more effectively.

WHO & HOW: Software selection should be a joint venture involving key users as well as Management Information Systems (MIS) people. This step must be accomplished relatively quickly and can be done so via the effective use of available information about manufacturing and distribution software. (For more information, see *The Standard System*, 1989 Oliver Wight Limited Publications, Inc.).

TIME FRAME: Several days to several weeks.

MRP II
Proven Path Detailed Implementation Plan

TASK	RESPONSIBLE	COMMENTS
12. SOFTWARE	MIS Mgr.	Select and implement the software to support the planning and control systems identified above.
A. Select software.	MIS Mgr. P&IC Mfg. Suprvsn.	Select software that meets most of the needs from a user and MIS point of view.
1. Acquire *The Standard System* book.	MIS Mgr. P&IC Mfg. Suprvsn.	Available from Oliver Wight Limited Publications, this book provides an explanation of what a typical software package should provide.
2. If needed, schedule software consulting audit.	MIS Mgr. P&IC Mfg. Suprvsn.	Helpful in situations where new software is being used or extensive modification and/or interfacing is required.
B. Evaluate systems work and acquire necessary resources.	MIS Mgr.	Includes work needed for modifications, interfacing, and temporary bridges.
C. Implement necessary modules with modifications and interfacing.	MIS Mgr.	Typical modules include: Inventory Transactions, Bills of Material, Routings, Master Production Scheduling, Material Requirements Planning, Capacity Requirements Planning, Shop Floor Control, Input Output Control, Purchasing, Financial Integration.
D. Agree on MIS performance standards.	MIS Mgr. P&IC Mfg. Suprvsn.	Response times, on-time completion of planning run, reports, etc.

13. PILOT AND CUTOVER[6] (MRP II)

DEFINITION: Conversion of the current process to the new process.

PURPOSE: To prove that the new tool actually works and to begin to benefit from it.

WHO & HOW: The people directly involved with the implementation begin to operate their part of the business using the new systems and/or processes.

TIME FRAME: Several weeks to several months.

---

[6] Cutover applies only to company-wide implementations. It entails adding the rest of the products/items onto the system folowing a successful operation of the pilot.

MRP II
Proven Path Detailed Implementation Plan

TASK	RESPONSIBLE	COMMENTS
13. PILOT AND CUTOVER		
A. Complete three pilots.	Team Leader Project Team Involved Users	Conversion of the current processes to the new processes using a pilot approach.
	Team Leader Project Team Involved Users	Pilots are: 1. Computer pilot to test the software. 2. Conference room pilot to test procedures and people's understanding. 3. Live pilot to test the new processes and verify they are working. Systems that are typically implemented using the pilot approach are: 1. Master Production Scheduling. 2. Material Requirements Planning. 3. Shop Floor Control. 4. Supplier Scheduling and Development.
B. Monitor critical measurements.	Team Leader	Before moving into cutover, verify that the new processes and systems are working.
C. Group remaining products into several groups.	P&IC Involved Users	Three or four groups are typical.
D. Bring each group onto the new systems.	P&IC	Each group will require intense planner coverage to get them settled down.

38

14. PERFORMANCE MEASUREMENTS (MRP II)

DEFINITION: Comparison of actual results to previously established key performance variables.

PURPOSE: To verify that the changes are delivering the expected results, and to provide feedback for implementation corrections.

WHO & HOW: This step should be done by people directly involved in the implementation, perhaps with assistance from other departments, such as MIS, accounting, etc.

TIME FRAME: Duration of the pilot and/or cutover phase.

15. Audit Assessment II (MRP II)

DEFINITION: Analysis of the company's situation, problems, and opportunities in light of the newly implemented tool(s).

PURPOSE: To verify the effectiveness of the newly implemented tools, and to define the next steps on the continuing improvement journey.

There is another critically important step. Under no circumstances should it be skipped, since one of its missions is to define the next improvement initiative to follow. Should this step be omitted, the company's drive for operational excellence will stall out, and the company will be left in a competitively vulnerable position.

WHO & HOW: Participants in this step include the executives, a wide range of operating managers, and, in virtually all cases, outside consultants with Class A credentials in MRP II, JIT/TQC, and/or DRP.

The process is one of fact finding, identifying areas of consensus and disagreement, matching the company's current status and strategies with the tools it has available for execution. The end result should be the development of an action plan to move the company onto a path of continuous improvement.

TIME FRAME: One week to one month.

16. ONGOING EDUCATION (MRP II)

DEFINITION: A continuing effort to upgrade everyone's awareness
and skills.

PURPOSE: To emphasize the importance of people's jobs and to
increase their abilities to do them. Ongoing education
reinforces initial education as well as being necessary
for new employees and employees in new jobs.

WHO & HOW: Department managers and supervisors are responsible
for helping their people grow. Aids, such as videotapes, contribute to the effectiveness of the education
program.

TIME FRAME: Forever.

MRP II

Proven Path Detailed Implementation Plan

TASK	RESPONSIBLE	COMMENTS
14. PERFORMANCE MEASURE-MENTS	Dept. Heads	Compare actual results to the previously agreed-upon key measurements. Typical performance measurements include: 1. Production Plan performance. 2. Master Production Schedule performance. 3. Manufacturing Schedule performance. 4. Engineering Schedule performance. 5. Supplier Delivery performance. Other measurements include: 1. Customer Service. 2. Quality. 3. Cost. 4. Velocity.
15. AUDIT/ASSESSMENT II	Top Mgmt. Middle Mgmt.	Re-assess the company's situation. Where are the current opportunities, what needs to be done next. This could be a phase 2 of the implementation, a concentrated effort to improve current levels of performance, etc. In most cases, this is done with the help of an outside consultant with Class A credentials.
16. ONGOING EDUCATION	Dept. Heads	Run a continuing program of outside education and business meetings to improve skill levels and company operating results.
A. Educate key managers new to the business.	Top Mgmt.	New managers in key positions need exposure at either the Top Management Course or Five Day Course to continue achieving full operating benefits.

42

MRP II

Proven Path Detailed Implementation Plan

TASK	RESPONSIBLE	COMMENTS
B. Maintain in-house experts.	Dept. Heads	Also important to continue achieving full operating benefits.
C. Continue the series of business meetings.	Dept. Heads	These meetings focus on how to improve the operating results of the business through the use of these tools. It's good to stand back and look at the situation from time to time. Sometimes new people are run through a special series of meetings, more typically, they are included in the ongoing series of business meetings.

43

Although some steps can be done quickly, while others require considerable time, it is essential to complete each step if the full potential of MRP II, JIT/TQC, and DRP is to be attained. Nevertheless, general managers who confront major problems are often anxious to achieve improvements, and may not insist on a vision statement, a cost/benefit analysis, or a description of the new sales, logistics, and manufacturing processes. These executives need to resist the temptation to minimize the importance of the 16 steps—the success of the company's goals are tied directly to how well each activity is carried out.

Now, keeping the generalized Proven Path in mind, let's look at the Fast-Track Implementation approaches.

Anatomy of the Proven Path—Just-in-Time/Total Quality Control (JIT/TQC)

The Proven Path encompasses 16 basic steps, regardless of whether you're implementing MRP II, JIT/TQC, or DRP, and whether you're using a Fast-Track approach or following a standard company-wide implementation.

Naturally, the time frame will vary from company to company depending on its size, complexity, and competitive posture.

The implementation steps are the same for a company-wide or a Fast-Track approach. Understanding and following each step with dedication leads to Class A results. The following pages explain each of the components in the Proven Path chart. This chart is contained on the inside back cover of this book in a convenient fold-out format, which allows reference to the chart while also being able to read the book.

The explanations for MRP II, Just-in-Time/Total Quality Control (JIT/TQC), and DRP are each contained in a separate section, and each includes a detailed implementation plan. This detailed implementation plan is an improved version of the Oliver Wight Detailed Implementation Plan, which has been used by thousands of companies over the last 15 years. What needs to be done is for you to tailor the plan to your company:

1. Cross off any tasks you have already completed.

2. Add any tasks that are individual to your company's implementation.

3. Replace the generalized job titles in the plan with the names of the people in your company responsible for the different tasks.

4. Add dates. The general time frame is included in the explanation of each Proven Path element. It's up to you to develop the start and due dates for each element as well as the tasks within each element.

Appendix B is a sample of what a tailored implementation plan would look like.

Many companies today are simultaneously implementing several of these management tools, or overlapping the implementations. For example, a company may be implementing DRP and MRP II. The Proven Path approach makes it easy to integrate these implementations because the implementation approach is the same for all. To illustrate this, let's look at combining the detailed implementation plans for MRP II and JIT/TQC. This would involve the following:

1. Combine similar implementation tasks. Rather than writing a vision statement for MRP II alone, write one for MRP II and JIT/TQC. Rather than setting performance goals for MRP II alone, set them for both MRP II and JIT/TQC.

2. List separately those implementation tasks that do not overlap. For example, there would be an implementation task for the JIT Breakthrough Pilot and a task for the MRP pilots (software, conference room, and live).

3. Modify the tasks in situations where simultaneous or overlapping implementations alter the tasks. One example of this is in the area of inventory record accuracy: Some provision will have to be made for JIT/TQC point-of-use storage, which might not be the case for an

MRP II-only implementation. These tasks are clearly identified in the comments sections of the detailed implementation plans.

The same approach would be used to combine DRP and MRP II, or any other combination of these implementations.

There are a number of abbreviations used in the RESPONSIBLE column of the detailed implementation plans. The table below shows these abbreviations and their meaning:

Dept.	Department
Distr.	Distribution
Engr.	Engineering (either Design or Manufacturing)
Exec.	Executive
Mgmt.	Management
Mgr.	Manager
MIS	Management Information Systems
P&IC	Production & Inventory Control
Suprvsn.	Supervision

1. Audit/Assessment I (JIT/TQC)

DEFINITION: An analysis of the company's current situation, problems, opportunities, strategies, etc. The analysis will serve as the basis for putting together an action plan.

PURPOSE: To determine which tools are specifically needed, and in what order they should be implemented. For example, a company may believe that it needs a new MRP II system. This may be true, but the analysis may reveal that because of substantial inventories in the field, implementing a DRP system first will provide the greatest payback. Once DRP is up and running, the company can focus on the incremental gain from a new MRP II system.

This step and its companion, audit/assessment II, are critically important to ensure that the improvement initiatives to be pursued by the company match its true needs; that they will generate competitive advantages in the short run; and that they will be consistent with the company's long-term strategy.

WHO & HOW: Participants in this step include the executives, a wide range of operating managers, and, in virtually all cases, outside consultants with Class A credentials in MRP II, JIT/TQC, and/or DRP.

The process is one of fact finding, identifying areas of consensus and disagreement, and matching the company's current status and strategies with the tools it has available for execution. The end result will be the development of an action plan to move the company onto a path of continuous improvement.

TIME FRAME: Several days to one month.[7] Please note: The audit/ assessment is not a prolonged, multi-month affair involving a detailed documentation of current systems. Rather, its focus and thrust is on what's NOT working well and what needs to be done to become more competitive.

[7] Time Frame as used in this document refers to elapsed time, not workdays of applied effort. In this specific instance, the number of workdays would typically range from two to eight.

2. FIRST-CUT EDUCATION (JIT/TQC)

DEFINITION: Key people must learn how the approaches work as specified by audit/assessment I: what they consist of; how they operate; and what is required to implement and use them properly.

PURPOSE: To provide a basic understanding of the approach to be pursued so the group can 1) complete a cost/benefit analysis, 2) provide the leadership necessary for the implementation, and 3) understand how to manage successfully when the new tools are available.

WHO & HOW: A small group of executives and managers (perhaps a dozen people) attend a public seminar on the approach being considered.1

TIME FRAME: One to four weeks.

Note: Some executives may go through first-cut education prior to audit/ assessment I. Either they will not be aware of the value of this step, or may want to become familiar with MRP II, JIT/TQC, and DRP prior to the audit/assessment. The order is not important; the critical issue is to make sure that both steps are done.

3. VISION STATEMENT (JIT/TQC)

DEFINITION: A written document that defines the desired operational environment. It answers the question: What do we want to accomplish?

PURPOSE: To provide a framework for consistent decision making, and to serve as a rallying point for the whole company.

WHO & HOW: The executives and managers who participated in first-cut education, in one or several meetings, hammer out what the company will look like and what new competitive capabilities it will have after the new approach has been implemented.

TIME FRAME: One to several days.

4. COST/BENEFIT (JIT/TQC)

DEFINITION: A written document that spells out the costs of imple-
                   mentation and the benefits of operating at a Class A
                   level.

PURPOSE: To make possible an informed decision about whether
                   to proceed with the implementation; to build a founda-
                   tion for the project; and to ensure there is buy-in and
                   commitment from management to provide the neces-
                   sary resources.

WHO & HOW: Involves the same people and often the same meetings
                   as the vision statement. The top person from each
                   functional area should be accountable for providing
                   the estimate of benefits and the eventual achievement
                   of them.

TIME FRAME: One day to one week.

5. PROJECT ORGANIZATION (JIT/TQC)

DEFINITION: Creation of the appropriate management and operational level team(s). Generally, this consists of a steering committee of executives and a project team of key users.

PURPOSE: To assign responsibilities and allocate people resources to the project.

WHO & HOW: Initially, much the same group as above to do the job of identifying candidates. Afterwards, certain executives and managers discuss the opportunity with the candidates to gain their acceptance of the assignment.

TIME FRAME: One day to two weeks.

6. PERFORMANCE GOALS (JIT/TQC)

DEFINITION: Agreement of what performance categories are expected to improve and what levels they are expected to reach.

PURPOSE: To identify improvements that are expected to be achieved and how they will be measured.

WHO & HOW: Essentially the same people who attended first-cut education use the knowledge gained there to set specific targets for attainment (e.g., customer delivery performance, lead time reduction, schedule compliance, cost reduction, productivity increases, inventory reductions, etc.).

TIME FRAME: One hour to one day.

Please note: In many cases it's possible for most of the activities specified in Steps 3, 4, 5, and 6 to be accomplished by the same people in the same several meetings. This is good, since there is an urgency to get started, and time is of the essence.

Just-in-Time/Total Quality Control (JIT/TQC) Proven Path Detailed Implementation Plan

TASK	RESPONSIBLE	COMMENTS
1. AUDIT/ASSESSMENT I	Top Mgmt. Middle Mgmt.	Assess the company's current situation. In most cases, this is done with the help of an outside consultant with Class A credentials.
2. FIRST-CUT EDUCATION	Top Mgmt. Middle Mgmt.	Learn the philosophy and the process of JIT/TQC. Understand why it is essential to compete in the future. Have top managers attend the JIT/TQC Top Management Course. Key middle managers should attend the JIT/TQC Implementation Class.
3. VISION STATEMENT	Top Mgmt. Middle Mgmt.	A short, concise document defining what the company wants to accomplish in the JIT/TQC Breakthrough Pilot.
4. COST/BENEFIT	Top Mgmt. Middle Mgmt.	A clear estimate of the costs and benefits, developed by a cross-functional management team.
A. Prepare cost/benefit.	Top Mgmt. Middle Mgmt.	Cost/benefit analysis (typically begun in the JIT/TQC Implementation Class).
B. Commit to implementation.	Top Mgmt.	Approve the Breakthrough Pilot process. Communicate the commitment to JIT/TQC. Repeat clear, consistent messages.
5. PROJECT ORGANIZATION	Top Mgmt.	Create the appropriate management and operational teams. Even though JIT/TQC is a continuous effort, these teams are intended to manage the implementation until JIT/TQC becomes a way of life.
A. Executive Steering Committee.	Top Mgmt.	A group of selected top managers formed to provide strategic leadership and support for the JIT/TQC implementation. This committee must include the Executive Torchbearer (champion). Schedule review meetings once a month.

Just-in-Time/Total Quality Control (JIT/TQC)
Proven Path Detailed Implementation Plan

TASK	RESPONSIBLE	COMMENTS
B. Project Team (same group as the JIT Implementation Team).	Middle Mgmt.	This is the team that has the charter to implement the Breakthrough Pilot and drive JIT/TQC until it becomes a way of life at the company. Team Leader should be full-time.
C. Outside counsel.	Top Mgmt.	Benefit from the experience of an outside consultant with Class A experience to safely and economically accelerate competitive results.
6. PERFORMANCE GOALS	Top Mgmt. Middle Mgmt.	Using the ABCD Checklist and the Breakthrough Pilot criteria, agree on expected performance levels and measurements for the Breakthrough Pilot area. Typical performance measurements include: 1. Delivery: linearity, and delivery to customer promise dates. 2. Quality: parts per million, and cost of quality. 3. Inventory: days of supply and return on assets. 4. Velocity: days of lead time manufacturing, purchase, customer, and design.

7. INITIAL EDUCATION (JIT/TQC)

DEFINITION: An educational effort for all people who are involved in designing and using the new tools.

PURPOSE: To provide a basic understanding of what the company is striving to achieve, why it is important, and how it will enable them to do their jobs more effectively.

WHO & HOW: The groups(s) selected to manage the project (Step 5) must first become more knowledgeable on the approaches. This is usually accomplished through seminars and internal education sessions. These people would then lead the education of the larger group. Business discussions led by managers and supervisors, and assisted by videotapes, have proven to be a practical and effective method of accomplishing this step.

TIME FRAME: Throughout the implementation schedule.

8. THE SALES, LOGISTICS, AND MANUFACTURING PROCESSES (JIT/TQC)

DEFINITION: Detailed statement of how the Sales/Marketing, Logistics, and Manufacturing functions will perform following implementation, and the detailed project plan necessary to achieve this.

PURPOSE: To ensure that the details of the implementation will be consistent with the vision statement; to verify that the processes that will be affected by the upcoming changes will be prioritized based on those most in need of improvement; and to create the detailed schedule necessary for effective project management.

WHO & HOW: Key people who will be directly involved lay out the detailed project schedule and, where appropriate, obtain concurrence from senior management.

TIME FRAME: One week to two months.

Just-in-Time/Total Quality Control (JIT/TQC)
Proven Path Detailed Implementation Plan

TASK	RESPONSIBLE	COMMENTS
7. INITIAL EDUCATION	Team Leader	Provide the necessary understanding to all people who will be involved in JIT/TQC. Everyone should be exposed to the basics of JIT/TQC at the onset of the program.
A. Outside education for the Project Team.	Team Leader	To be effective leaders, these people need to gain a detailed understanding of JIT/TQC principles at the JIT/TQC Implementation Course.
B. Steering Committee.	Team Leader	All members who have not previously attended should now complete the JIT Top Management Class.
C. Video Education for Steering Committee and Project Team.	Team Leader	A series of business meetings where the managers apply the concepts to their company. While the initial focus is usually the implementation of the Breakthrough Pilot, these meetings may address the application of JIT/TQC throughout the entire business.
D. Pilot-level education and training.	Team Leader and Task Team Leader	A continuation of the business meetings where the general principles are translated into the specifics of operation for the Breakthrough Pilot This education involves selecting implementation alternatives, and detailing the necessary changes. It also includes training in the mechanics of the new processes.
8. SALES, LOGISTICS, AND MANUFACTURING PROCESSES	Top Mgmt. Middle Mgmt.	Develop plans of how these operations will operate in relation to the Breakthrough Pilot.

9. PLANNING AND CONTROL PROCESSES (JIT/TQC)

DEFINITION: Identification of all systems and processes necessary for effective planning and control, from sales & operations planning down through detailed plant, supplier, and distribution schedules.

PURPOSE: To ensure that the formal planning and control systems either in place or to be implemented are capable of generating and maintaining valid plans and schedules for:

1. Shipment of customer orders
2. Logistics
3. Manufacturing
4. Purchasing
5. Engineering
6. Finance

WHO & HOW: The people throughout the company, in marketing and sales, manufacturing, purchasing, engineering, planning, and elsewhere who will be involved in generating plans and schedules, or in executing them. They do this by using their knowledge of the present operating environment of the company with the knowledge they gained in initial education as to what is required.

TIME FRAME: One week to three months.

Just-in-Time/Total Quality Control (JIT/TQC)
Proven Path Detailed Implementation Plan

TASK	RESPONSIBLE	COMMENTS
9. PLANNING AND CONTROL PROCESSES		Identification of any changes that should be made to the planning and control systems in the Breakthrough Pilot area to support JIT/TQC.

61

10. DATA MANAGEMENT (JIT/TQC)

DEFINITION: Attaining necessary levels of data accuracy and structure, with timely reporting.

PURPOSE: To make decisions based on current, accurate information.

WHO & HOW: Accountability for data integrity must be assigned.

Data	People
Inventory Record Accuracy	Warehouse and Stockroom Personnel
Bill of Material[8] Accuracy and Structure	Product Engineering, Research and Development, Distribution
Routings (if required)	Manufacturing/Industrial Engineering

TIME FRAME: Up to several months.

---

[8] Often called formulas, recipes, practices, etc. in process flow manufacturing. In a
DRP implementation, this step would refer to the distribution bill of material (i.e., which
products are stocked at which locations in the distribution network).

Just-in-Time/Total Quality Control (JIT/TQC)
Proven Path Detailed Implementation Plan

TASK	RESPONSIBLE	COMMENTS
10. DATA MANAGEMENT		
A. Inventory Record Accuracy.	Stockroom Mgr. Mfg. Suprvsn.	These are the steps to maintain high levels of data integrity in the Breakthrough Pilot area. Changes need to be made to maintain accuracy when using point-of-use and point-of-manufacture storage. Changes are also made in the who, how, and when of cycle counting.
B. Bill of Material Accuracy.	Engr. Mgr. Mfg. Suprvsn.	Typical areas of work include: 1. Flattening the bills of material as a result of simplifying the product and processes. 2. Noting where material is used, for use in postdeduct transactions (backflushing).
C. Routing Accuracy.	Mfg. Engr. Mgr.	Typical activities include simplifying the routings to represent acceler-ated product flows and the creation of cells.

63

11. Process Improvement (JIT/TQC)

Definition: Continuous improvement of all processes for sales, operations, logistics and product design.

Purpose: To ensure survival, growth, and prosperity as a business. This is done by changing those processes that inhibit progress and/or are incompatible with the new vision.

Who & How: Initially, only those people involved with the actual implementation, but eventually everyone in the company, should participate in this step. This is done by creating within the organization a deep commitment to continuing improvement, a creative discontent with the status quo.

Time Frame: Never ending.

TASK	RESPONSIBLE	COMMENTS
11. PROCESS IMPROVEMENT		Create a model of the future factory to help people understand and accept the forthcoming changes. Demonstrate the new procedures and breakthrough results.
A. Develop implementation plans for the Breakthrough Pilot	Project Team	Typical activities are listed below.
1. Establish performance measures.	Project Team	Establish a benchmark to measure success based upon performance goals established.
2. Establish process layout.	Project Team	Determine manufacturing process and product flow within the pilot areas. Where economical, move equipment.
3. Establish material flow.	Project Team	Determine material flow to and from the pilot area from other areas not included in the pilot.
4. Establish kanban system for controlling production and material replenishment in the pilot area.	Project Team	Use of kanban is essential to the JIT process of "one less at a time." Establish kanban as the formal procedure for controlling production and authorizing material replenishment in the pilot area.
5. Define rules for common equipment.	Project Team	Some equipment may be required for traditional production as well as JIT production. Use information outlined in the implementation class to define how to share this equipment.
6. Establish quantity and plan for control of material stored at point of use.	Project Team Production People	When material is stored at point of manufacture/use, responsibility for controlling this material shifts to production. Develop training and accuracy verification procedures.

Just-in-Time/Total Quality Control (JIT/TQC)
Proven Path Detailed Implementation Plan

TASK	RESPONSIBLE	COMMENTS
7. Develop system interfaces.	Project Team	Develop procedural changes that will result in minimal software changes, yet will enable the pilot to operate according to the breakthrough specifications. An experienced consultant is critical at this stage.
8. Define points for material deduction.	Project Team	Determine where material will be postdeducted to maintain financial accountability.
9. Define engineering change procedure.	Project Team	When work orders are used, an engineering change is communicated to production via the work order. Without work orders, the changeover has to be done physically on the factory floor.
10. Define labor-collection procedures.	Project Team	Without work orders, how will labor be collected? Most companies use labor reporting by exception.
11. Decide how to bleed off excess inventory.	Project Team	When JIT/TQC is started, most companies quickly find they have more inventory in the pipeline than is required. The severity of the excess often dictates the need for a strategy to bleed off the excess while making constructive use of people's time.

12. SOFTWARE SELECTION (JIT/TQC)

DEFINITION: Acquisition of software for planning, control, execu-
                tion, analysis, and monitoring.

PURPOSE: To provide the information that supports the users in
                doing their jobs more effectively.

WHO & HOW: Software selection should be a joint venture involving
                key users as well as MIS people. This step must be
                accomplished relatively quickly and can be done so
                via the effective use of available information about
                manufacturing and distribution software. (For more
                information, see *The Standard System,* 1989 Oliver
                Wight Limited Publications, Inc.).

TIME FRAME: Several days to several weeks.

Just-in-Time/Total Quality Control (JIT/TQC)
Proven Path Detailed Implementation Plan

TASK	RESPONSIBLE	COMMENTS
12. SOFTWARE	MIS Mgr.	Make essential software changes identified by the Project Team that are needed to enable the pilot to operate according to the breakthrough specifications.

13. PILOT AND CUTOVER[9] (JIT/TQC)

DEFINITION: Conversion of the current process to the new process.

PURPOSE: To prove that the new tool actually works and to begin
                 to benefit from it.

WHO & HOW: The people directly involved with the implementation
                 begin to operate their part of the business using the
                 new systems and/or processes.

TIME FRAME: Several weeks to several months.

---

[9] Cutover applies only to company-wide implementations. It entails adding the rest of the
products/items onto the system following a successful operation of the pilot.

Just-in-Time/Total Quality Control (JIT/TQC) Proven Path Detailed Implementation Plan

TASK	RESPONSIBLE	COMMENTS
13. PILOT AND CUTOVER	Project Team	Conversion of the current processes to the new processes using a pilot approach. Creating a model to demonstrate the effectiveness of the vision.
A. Begin JIT/TQC in pilot area.	Project Team	The Breakthrough Pilot is the recommended approach to implementing JIT/TQC and should be ready to begin operation within 120 days. Typical activities are listed below.
1. Practice JIT.	Project Team	Become familiar with the mechanics of the kanban technique, then begin to practice JIT's "one less at a time" process by carefully removing kanbans.
2. Practice TQC.	Project Team	When the JIT process exposes a constraint, eliminate the constraint using TQC's "Plan, Do, Check, Action" process.
3. Start formal set-up reduction process.	Production Task Team	Where equipment setups are or projected to be a constraint, follow the "SMED" process. Use videotaping.
4. Begin monitoring and displaying performance measurements.	Project Team	Post performance measurements in a prominent place in the pilot area. Use run type charts to show progress plus Pareto Charts to point the way to improvement.
5. Put flip chart in pilot area to collect problems/suggestions.	Top Mgmt. Middle Mgmt. Project Team Production People	Provide an easy and efficient way for everyone to communicate ideas to eliminate waste. Management must ensure that a responsive answer is provided for each idea, but responsibility and authority should be delegated to the lowest level capable of responding to each idea.

70

14. PERFORMANCE MEASUREMENTS (JIT/TQC)

DEFINITION: Comparison of actual results to previously established key performance variables.

PURPOSE: To verify that the changes are delivering the expected results, and to provide feedback for implementation corrections.

WHO & HOW: This step should be done by people directly involved in the implementation, perhaps with assistance from other departments, such as MIS, accounting, etc.

TIME FRAME: Duration of the pilot and/or cutover phase.

15. Audit Assessment II (JIT/TQC)

DEFINITION: Analysis of the company's situation, problems, and
                   opportunities in light of the newly implemented
                   tool(s).

PURPOSE: To verify the effectiveness of the newly implemented
                   tools, and to define the next steps on the continuing
                   improvement journey.
                       This is another critically important step. Under no
                   circumstances should it be skipped, since one of its
                   missions is to define the next improvement initiative to
                   follow. Should this step be omitted, the company's
                   drive for operational excellence will stall out, and the
                   company will be left in a competitively vulnerable
                   position.

WHO & HOW: Participants in this step include the executives, a wide
                   range of operating managers, and, in virtually all
                   cases, outside consultants with Class A credentials in
                   MRP II, JIT/TQC, and/or DRP.
                       The process is one of fact finding, identifying areas
                   of consensus and disagreement, matching the com-
                   pany's current status and strategies with the tools it has
                   available for execution. The end result should be the
                   development of an action plan to move the company
                   onto a path of continuous improvement.

TIME FRAME: One week to one month.

16. ONGOING EDUCATION (JIT/TQC)

DEFINITION: A continuing effort to upgrade everyone's awareness and skills.

PURPOSE: To emphasize the importance of people's jobs and to increase their abilities to do them. Ongoing education reinforces initial education as well as being necessary for new employees and employees in new jobs.

WHO & HOW: Department managers and supervisors are responsible for helping their people grow. Aids, such as videotapes, contribute to the effectiveness of the education program.

TIME FRAME: Forever.

Just-in-Time/Total Quality Control (JIT/TQC)
Proven Path Detailed Implementation Plan

TASK	RESPONSIBLE	COMMENTS
6. Establish daily production floor meeting.	Project Team Production Supr.	Most people meet once per shift. Provides ability to communicate opportunities for improvement to those who can eliminate the root cause of the problem. Use problems documented on the flip chart as basis for discussion.
14. PERFORMANCE MEASUREMENTS	Dept. Heads	Compare actual results to the previously agreed-upon key measurements.
A. Evaluate results of pilot.	Top Mgmt.	"Go on/go back" checkpoint. Review actual results against expected performance levels.
15. AUDIT/ASSESSMENT II	Top Mgmt. Middle Mgmt.	Re-assess the company's situation. Is it now time to implement JIT/TQC across the company? When should suppliers and/or customers be involved? What's next? In most cases, this is done with the help of an outside consultant with Class A credentials.
16. ONGOING EDUCATION		Ongoing education for the Breakthrough Pilot typically means initial education for the next phase of implementation.

17. First-Cut Education (JIT/TQC)

DEFINITION: Key people must learn how the approaches work as specified by audit/assessment I: what they consist of; how they operate; and what is required to implement and use them properly.

PURPOSE: To provide a basic understanding of the approach to be pursued so the group can 1) complete a cost/benefit analysis, 2) provide the leadership necessary for the implementation, and 3) understand how to manage successfully when the new tools are available.

WHO & HOW: A small group of executives and managers (perhaps a dozen people) attend a public seminar on the approach being considered.

TIME FRAME: One to four weeks.

Note: Some executives may go through first-cut education prior to audit/assessment I. Either they will not be aware of the value of this step, or may want to become familiar with MRP II, JIT/TQC, and DRP prior to the audit/assessment. The order is not important; the critical issue is to make sure that both steps are done.

18. Vision Statement (JIT/TQC)

DEFINITION: A written document that defines the desired opera-
                  tional environment. It answers the question: What do
                  we want to accomplish?

PURPOSE: To provide a framework for consistent decision mak-
                  ing, and to serve as a rallying point for the whole
                  company.

WHO & HOW: The executives and managers who participated in
                  first-cut education, in one or several meetings, ham-
                  mer out what the company will look like and what new
                  competitive capabilities it will have after the new
                  approach has been implemented.

TIME FRAME: One to several days.

19. Cost/Benefit (JIT/TQC)

DEFINITION: A written document that spells out the costs of imple-
                mentation and the benefits of operating at a Class A
                level.

PURPOSE: To make possible an informed decision about whether
                to proceed with the implementation; to build a founda-
                tion for the project; and to ensure there is buy-in and
                commitment from management to provide the neces-
                sary resources.

WHO & HOW: Involves the same people and often the same meetings
                as the vision statement. The top person from each
                functional area should be accountable for providing
                the estimate of benefits and the eventual achievement
                of them.

TIME FRAME: One day to one week.

20. PROJECT ORGANIZATION (JIT/TQC)

DEFINITION: Creation of the appropriate management and opera-
                 tional level team(s). Generally, this consists of a steer-
                 ing committee of executives and a project team of key
                 users.

PURPOSE: To assign responsibilities and allocate people re-
                 sources to the project.

WHO & HOW: Initially, much the same group as above to do the job
                 of identifying candidates. Afterwards, certain execu-
                 tives and managers discuss the opportunity with the
                 candidates to gain their acceptance of the assignment.

TIME FRAME: One day to two weeks.

21. PERFORMANCE GOALS (JIT/TQC)

DEFINITION: Agreement of what performance categories are expected to improve and what levels they are expected to reach.

PURPOSE: To identify improvements that are expected to be achieved and how they will be measured.

WHO & HOW: Essentially the same people who attended first-cut education use the knowledge gained there to set specific targets for attainment (e.g., customer delivery performance, lead time reduction, schedule compliance, cost reduction, productivity increases, inventory reductions, etc.).

TIME FRAME: One hour to one day.

Please note: In many cases it's possible for most of the activities specified in Steps 3, 4, 5, and 6 to be accomplished by the same people in the same several meetings. This is good, since there is an urgency to get started, and time is of the essence.

Just-in-Time/Total Quality Control (JIT/TQC)
Proven Path Detailed Implementation Plan

TASK	RESPONSIBLE	COMMENTS
17. FIRST-CUT EDUCATION	Top Mgmt. Middle Mgmt.	In most cases, first-cut education was completed before the Breakthrough Pilot. Do any additional education as needed.
18. VISION STATEMENT	Top Mgmt. Middle Mgmt.	Prepare a "white paper," based on the insights gained from the Breakthrough Pilot. The document should thoroughly describe the company changes that will occur in the next five years as JIT/TQC drives continuous improvement.
19. COST/BENEFIT	Top Mgmt. Middle Mgmt.	Refine the cost/benefit analysis based on the results of the Breakthrough Pilot.
A. Prepare cost/benefit.	Top Mgmt. Middle Mgmt.	Revise as needed.
20. PROJECT ORGANIZATION	Top Mgmt.	Create the appropriate management and operational teams.
A. Executive Steering Committee.	Top Mgmt.	Most companies keep the same Steering Committee created for the Breakthrough Pilot.
B. Project Team	Middle Mgmt.	Most companies keep the same Project Team created for the Breakthrough Pilot.
C. Outside counsel.	Top Mgmt.	Most companies continue to use the same outside consultant.
D. Execution teams.	Exec. Steering Committee	Identify the sequence of products and/or processes to be implemented.
21. PERFORMANCE GOALS	Top Mgmt. Middle Mgmt.	Using the ABCD Checklist, revise the expected performance levels and measurements based on the results of the Breakthrough Pilot.

22. INITIAL EDUCATION (JIT/TQC)

DEFINITION: An educational effort for all people who are involved in designing and using the new tools.

PURPOSE: To provide a basic understanding of what the company is striving to achieve, why it is important, and how it will enable them to do their jobs more effectively.

WHO & HOW: The groups(s) selected to manage the project (Step 5) must first become more knowledgeable on the approaches. This is usually accomplished through seminars and internal education sessions. These people would then lead the education of the larger group. Business discussions led by managers and supervisors, and assisted by videotapes, have proven to be a practical and effective method of accomplishing this step.

TIME FRAME: Throughout the implementation schedule.

23. THE SALES, LOGISTICS, AND MANUFACTURING PROCESSES (JIT/TQC)

DEFINITION:
Detailed statement of how the Sales/Marketing, Logistics, and Manufacturing functions will perform following implementation, and the detailed project plan necessary to achieve this.

PURPOSE:
To ensure that the details of the implementation will be consistent with the vision statement; to verify that the processes that will be affected by the upcoming changes will be prioritized based on those most in need of improvement; and to create the detailed schedule necessary for effective project management.

WHO & HOW:
Key people who will be directly involved lay out the detailed project schedule and, where appropriate, obtain concurrence from senior management.

TIME FRAME:
One week to two months.

Just-in-Time/Total Quality Control (JIT/TQC)
Proven Path Detailed Implementation Plan

TASK	RESPONSIBLE	COMMENTS
22. INITIAL EDUCATION	Team Leader	Provide the necessary understanding to all people who will be involved in JIT/TQC.
A. Outside education for people who will be leaders at the in-house series of business meetings, and key managers.	Team Leader	To be effective discussion leaders, these managers need exposure at either the JIT/TQC Top Management Course or the JIT/TQC Implementation Course. The key managers mentioned here are people critical to the design or operation, but who have not been involved in either the first cut (Task #2) or initial education (Tasks #7A and #7B) for the Breakthrough Pilot.
B. Discussion Leaders video course.	Team Leader	A series of business meetings where the general principles are translated into the specifics of operation for your company. These people become the discussion leaders for the team specific meetings.
C. Team specific video courses.	Discussion Leaders	Series of business meetings organized by execution teams. The objective is to determine specifically what changes need to be made to run the business differently.
D. Department-level education and training.	Dept. Mgrs.	This education is for the people doing the work in their areas. It involves selecting implementation alternatives, and detailing the necessary changes. It also includes training in the mechanics of the new processes.
23. SALES, LOGISTICS, AND MANUFACTURING PROCESSES	Top Mgmt. Middle Mgmt.	Refine the detailed statement of how these processes will operate following implementation (based on the results of the Breakthrough Pilot). The discussion leaders series of business meetings (Task #22B above) generally provides most of the information needed for this task.

83

24. Planning and Control Processes (JIT/TQC)

DEFINITION: Identification of all systems and processes necessary for effective planning and control, from sales & operations planning down through detailed plant, supplier and distribution schedules.

PURPOSE: To ensure that the formal planning and control systems either in place or to be implemented are capable of generating and maintaining valid plans and schedules for:

1. Shipment of customer orders
2. Logistics
3. Manufacturing
4. Purchasing
5. Engineering
6. Finance

WHO & HOW: The people throughout the company, in marketing and sales, manufacturing, purchasing, engineering, planning, and elsewhere who will be involved in generating plans and schedules, or in executing them. They do this by using their knowledge of the present operating environment of the company with the knowledge they gained in initial education as to what is required.

TIME FRAME: One week to three months.

Just-in-Time/Total Quality Control (JIT/TQC)
Proven Path Detailed Implementation Plan

TASK	RESPONSIBLE	COMMENTS
24. PLANNING AND CONTROL PROCESSES		
A. Sales & Operations Planning.	Top Mgmt.	Identification of any further changes that should be made to the planning and control systems in order to support JIT/TQC.
B. Demand Management.	Sales Mgr.	Do sales & operations planning on all products. Focus on eliminating or reducing detailed forecasting wherever possible by using JIT/TQC to become more flexible in building different product configurations. May also involve DRP for some companies.
C. Master Production Scheduling.	P&IC Mgr.	Implement mixed-model master scheduling. Focus on linearity and responsiveness.
D. Capacity Planning.	P&IC Mgr. Mfg. Suprvsn.	In most companies, detailed Capacity Requirements Planning can be eliminated, using only Rough-Cut Capacity Planning.
E. Shop Scheduling.	P&IC Mgr. Mfg. Suprvsn.	As kanban is implemented, traditional work-order-based shop floor control is gradually eliminated to the point where it may be completely replaced.

25. Data Management (JIT/TQC)

Definition: Attaining necessary levels of data accuracy and structure, with timely reporting.

Purpose: To make decisions based on current, accurate information.

Who & How: Accountability for data integrity must be assigned.

Data	People
Inventory Record Accuracy	Warehouse and Stockroom Personnel
Bill of Material[10] Accuracy and Structure	Product Engineering, Research and Development, Distribution
Routings (if required)	Manufacturing/Industrial Engineering

Time Frame: Up to several months.

---

[10] Often called formulas, recipes, practices, etc. in process flow manufacturing. In a DRP implementation, this step would refer to the distribution bill of material (i.e., which products are stocked at which locations in the distribution network).

Just-in-Time/Total Quality Control (JIT/TQC)
Proven Path Detailed Implementation Plan

TASK	RESPONSIBLE	COMMENTS
25. DATA MANAGEMENT		
A. Inventory Record Accuracy.	Stockroom Mgr.	These are the steps to maintain high levels of data integrity, while also simplifying the manufacturing process by eliminating waste.
		Changes need to be made to maintain accuracy when using point-of-use and point-of-manufacture storage. Changes are also made in the who, how, and when of cycle counting.
B. Bill of Material Accuracy.	Engr. Mgr. Mfg. Suprvsn.	Typical areas of work include: 1. Flattening the bills of material as a result of simplifying the product and processes. 2. Noting where material is used, for use in backflushing.
C. Routing Accuracy.	Mfg. Engr. Mgr.	Typical activities include simplifying the routings to represent simplified, accelerated product flows and the creation of cells.

87

26. PROCESS IMPROVEMENT (JIT/TQC)

DEFINITION: Continuous improvement of all processes for sales, operations, logistics, and product design.

PURPOSE: To ensure survival, growth, and prosperity as a business. This is done by changing those processes that inhibit progress and/or are incompatible with the new vision.

WHO & HOW: Initially, only those people involved with the actual implementation, but eventually everyone in the company, should participate in this step. This is done by creating within the organization a deep commitment to continuing improvement, a creative discontent with the status quo.

TIME FRAME: Never ending.

Just-in-Time/Total Quality Control (JIT/TQC)
Proven Path Detailed Implementation Plan

TASK	RESPONSIBLE	COMMENTS
26. PROCESS IMPROVEMENT		
A. Extend JIT/TQC implementation.	Execution Teams	Extend the model of the future factory. Link segments of the pipeline from raw material to the end customer. Change mind-set from "pilot" to implementing a new way of life to ensure a competitive future.
		Develop detailed plans to extend JIT/TQC to all areas of the company, into its supplier base, and, if applicable, into its customer base. Approach each new area in the same manner as the initial pilot.
		Examine measures and procedures used in the pilot. Reinforce or revise. Begin to standardize the procedures that were proven to be effective during the Breakthrough Pilot stage throughout the company.
B. Link to suppliers.	Purchasing Mgr.	Typical activities include: 1. Begin supplier quality program. 2. Hold supplier open house (supplier education day).
C. Link to customers.	Sales Mgr.	If applicable.
D. Re-align personnel policies and procedures.	Personnel Mgr.	JIT/TQC is designed to strengthen people. Only when a company's people are thinking about the right constraints, and they are equipped to solve problems, can a company expect to compete. Human Resources must plan for the positive, yet significant, people issues surrounding JIT/TQC and our ability to compete in the future. These issues include compensation, labor grades, employment stability, and training.
E. Envision next steps.	Engr. Mgr.	JIT/TQC provides a fertile environment to successfully, economically, and knowledgeably implement other competitive tools. JIT/TQC provides stepping stones to automation, design for manufacturability, activity-based costing, benchmarking, and computer-integrated manufacturing.

27. SOFTWARE SELECTION (JIT/TQC)

DEFINITION: Acquisition of software for planning, control, execu-
                 tion, analysis, and monitoring.

PURPOSE: To provide the information that supports the users in
                 doing their jobs more effectively.

WHO & HOW: Software selection should be a joint venture involving
                 key users as well as MIS people. This step must be
                 accomplished relatively quickly and can be done so
                 via the effective use of available information about
                 manufacturing and distribution software. (For more
                 information, see *The Standard System,* 1989 Oliver
                 Wight Limited Publications, Inc.).

TIME FRAME: Several days to several weeks.

Just-in-Time/Total Quality Control (JIT/TQC)
Proven Path Detailed Implementation Plan

TASK	RESPONSIBLE	COMMENTS
27. SOFTWARE	MIS Mgr.	Develop programs and implement changes that will effectively support the direction JIT/TQC is leading the company.
A. Acquire necessary resources to evaluate system changes.	MIS Mgr.	Typical changes include manufacturing with no work orders, simplified reporting of production activity, collection of production labor by exception, multiple inventory locations, frequent replanning, mixed model scheduling, and purchasing without purchase orders.
B. Implement necessary modifications.	MIS Mgr.	See list above.
C. Develop system interfaces.	MIS Mgr.	Procedural and software changes listed above typically require systems work to interface different business systems. Examine areas where the velocity of information is too slow to meet the needs of JIT/TQC.

28. PILOT AND CUTOVER[11] (JIT/TQC)

DEFINITION: Conversion of the current process to the new process.

PURPOSE: To prove that the new tool actually works and to begin to benefit from it.

WHO & HOW: The people directly involved with the implementation begin to operate their part of the business using the new systems and/or processes.

TIME FRAME: Several weeks to several months.

---

[11] Cutover applies only to company-wide implementations. It entails adding the rest of the products/items onto the system following a successful operation of the pilot.

Just-in-Time/Total Quality Control (JIT/TQC)
Proven Path Detailed Implementation Plan

TASK	RESPONSIBLE	COMMENTS
28. EXTENSION OF INITIAL PILOT	Execution Teams	Conversion of the current processes to the new processes using a pilot approach. This phase can be thought of as a series of "Breakthrough Pilots" until all of the company is operating with JIT/TQC. The implementation of each of these areas uses the same steps as in the Breakthrough Pilot.

93

29. Performance Measurements (JIT/TQC)

Definition: Comparison of actual results to previously established key performance variables.

Purpose: To verify that the changes are delivering the expected results, and to provide feedback for implementation corrections.

Who & How: This step should be done by people directly involved in the implementation, perhaps with assistance from other departments, such as MIS, accounting, etc.

Time Frame: Duration of the pilot and/or cutover phase.

30. Audit Assessment II (JIT/TQC)

DEFINITION: Analysis of the company's situation, problems, and opportunities in light of the newly implemented tool(s).

PURPOSE: To verify the effectiveness of the newly implemented tools, and to define the next steps on the continuing improvement journey.

This is another critically important step. Under no circumstances should it be skipped, since one of its missions is to define the next improvement initiative to follow. Should this step be omitted, the company's drive for operational excellence will stall out, and the company will be left in a competitively vulnerable position.

WHO & HOW: Participants in this step include the executives, a wide range of operating managers, and, in virtually all cases, outside consultants with Class A credentials in MRP II, JIT/TQC, and/or DRP.

The process is one of fact finding, identifying areas of consensus and disagreement, matching the company's current status and strategies with the tools it has available for execution. The end result should be the development of an action plan to move the company onto a path of continuous improvement.

TIME FRAME: One week to one month.

31. ONGOING EDUCATION (JIT/TQC)

DEFINITION: A continuing effort to upgrade everyone's awareness and skills.

PURPOSE: To emphasize the importance of people's jobs and to increase their abilities to do them. Ongoing education reinforces initial education as well as being necessary for new employees and employees in new jobs.

WHO & HOW: Department managers and supervisors are responsible for helping their people grow. Aids, such as videotapes, contribute to the effectiveness of the education program.

TIME FRAME: Forever.

Just-in-Time/Total Quality Control (JIT/TQC)
Proven Path Detailed Implementation Plan

TASK	RESPONSIBLE	COMMENTS
29. PERFORMANCE MEASUREMENTS	Dept. Heads	Compare actual results to the previously agreed-upon key measurements.
30. AUDIT/ASSESSMENT III	Top Mgmt. Middle Mgmt.	Re-assess the company's situation. Where are the current opportunities, where should the management focus be? How well are we practicing JIT/TQC? How can we improve? What are the next steps we should consider? In most cases, this is done with the help of an outside consultant with Class A credentials.
31. ONGOING EDUCATION	Dept. Heads	Develop a continuing program of outside education and business meetings to improve skill levels and company operating results.
A. Educate key managers new to the business.	Top Mgmt.	New managers in key positions need exposure at either the JIT/TQC Top Management Course or the JIT/TQC Implementation Course to continue achieving full operating benefits.
B. Continue the series of business meetings.	Dept. Heads	These meetings focus on how to improve the operating results of the business through the use of these tools. It's good to stand back and look at the situation from time to time. Sometimes new people are run through a special series of meetings; more typically, they are included into the ongoing series of business meetings.

97

Although some steps can be done quickly, while others require considerable time, it is essential to complete each step if the full potential of MRP II, JIT/TQC, and DRP is to be attained. Nevertheless, general managers who confront major problems are often anxious to achieve improvements, and may not insist on a vision statement, a cost/benefit analysis, or a description of the new sales, logistics, and manufacturing processes. These executives need to resist the temptation to minimize the importance of the 16 steps—the success of the company's goals are tied directly to how well each activity is carried out.

Now, keeping the generalized Proven Path in mind, let's look at the Fast-Track Implementation approaches.

Anatomy of
The Proven Path—DRP

The Proven Path encompasses 16 basic steps, regardless of whether you're implementing MRP II, JIT/TQC, or DRP, and whether you're using a Fast-Track approach or following a standard company-wide implementation.

Naturally, the time frame will vary from company to company depending on its size, complexity, and competitive posture.

The implementation steps are the same for a company-wide or a Fast-Track approach. Understanding and following each step with dedication leads to Class A results. The following pages explain each of the components in the Proven Path chart. This chart is contained on the inside back cover of this book in a convenient fold-out format, which allows reference to the chart while also being able to read the book.

The explanations for MRP II, Just-in-Time/Total Quality Control (JIT/TQC), and DRP are each contained in a separate section, and each includes a detailed implementation plan. This detailed implementation plan is an improved version of the Oliver Wight Detailed Implementation Plan which has been used by thousands of companies over the last 15 years. What needs to be done is for you to tailor the plan to your company:

99

1. Cross off any tasks you have already completed.

2. Add any tasks that are individual to your company's implementation.

3. Replace the generalized job titles in the plan with the names of the people in your company responsible for the different tasks.

4. Add dates. The general time frame is included in the explanation of each Proven Path element. It's up to you to develop the start and due dates for each element as well as the tasks within each element.

Appendix B is a sample of what a tailored implementation plan would look like.

Many companies today are simultaneously implementing several of these management tools, or overlapping the implementations. For example, a company may be implementing DRP and MRP II. The Proven Path approach makes it easy to integrate these implementations because the implementation approach is the same for all. To illustrate this, let's look at combining the detailed implementation plans for MRP II and JIT/TQC. This would involve the following:

1. Combine similar implementation tasks. Rather than writing a vision statement for MRP II alone, write one for MRP II and JIT/TQC. Rather than setting performance goals for MRP II alone, set them for both MRP II and JIT/TQC.

2. List separately those implementation tasks that do not overlap. For example, there would be an implementation task for the JIT Breakthrough Pilot and a task for the MRP II pilots (software, conference room, and live).

3. Modify the tasks in situations where simultaneous or overlapping implementations alter the tasks. One example of this is in the area of inventory record accuracy: some provision will have to be made for JIT/TQC point-of-use storage which might not be the case for an MRP II-only implementation. These tasks are clearly identified in the comments sections of the detailed implementation plans.

The same approach would be used to combine DRP and MRP II, or any other combination of these implementations.

There are a number of abbreviations used in the RESPONSIBLE column of the detailed implementation plans. The table below shows these abbreviations and their meaning:

Dept.	Department
Distr.	Distribution
Engr.	Engineering (either Design or Manufacturing)
Exec.	Executive
Mgmt.	Management
Mgr.	Manager
MIS	Management Information Systems
P&IC	Production & Inventory Control
Suprvsn.	Supervision

1. Audit/Assessment I (DRP)

DEFINITION: An analysis of the company's current situation, problems, opportunities, strategies, etc. The analysis will serve as the basis for putting together an action plan.

PURPOSE: To determine which tools are specifically needed, and in what order they should be implemented. For example, a company may believe that it needs a new MRP II system. This may be true, but the analysis may reveal that because of substantial inventories in the field, implementing a DRP system first will provide the greatest payback. Once DRP is up and running, the company can focus on the incremental gain from a new MRP II system.

This step and its companion, audit/assessment II, are critically important to ensure that the improvement initiatives to be pursued by the company match its true needs; that they will generate competitive advantages in the short run; and that they will be consistent with the company's long-term strategy.

WHO & HOW: Participants in this step include the executives, a wide range of operating managers, and in virtually all cases, outside consultants with Class A credentials in MRP II, JIT/TQC, and/or DRP.

The process is one of fact finding, identifying areas of consensus and disagreement, and matching the company's current status and strategies with the tools it has available for execution. The end result will be the development of an action plan to move the company onto a path of continuous improvement.

TIME FRAME: Several days to one month.[12] Please note: The audit/
assessment is not a prolonged, multi-month affair involving a detailed documentation of current systems.
Rather, its focus and thrust is on what's NOT working
well and what needs to be done to become more
competitive.

[12] Time Frame as used in this document refers to elapsed time, not workdays of applied
effort. In this specific instance, the number of workdays would typically range from two
to eight.

2. First-Cut Education (DRP)

DEFINITION: Key people must learn how the approaches work as specified by audit/assessment I: what they consist of; how they operate; and what is required to implement and use them properly.

PURPOSE: To provide a basic understanding of the approach to be pursued so the group can 1) complete a cost/benefit analysis, 2) provide the leadership necessary for the implementation, and 3) understand how to manage successfully when the new tools are available.

WHO & HOW: A small group of executives and managers (perhaps a dozen people) attend a public seminar on the approach being considered.

TIME FRAME: One to four weeks.

Note: Some executives may go through first-cut education prior to audit/assessment I. Either they will not be aware of the value of this step, or may want to become familiar with MRP II, JIT/TQC, and DRP prior to the audit/assessment. The order is not important; the critical issue is to make sure that both steps are done.

3. VISION STATEMENT (DRP)

DEFINITION: A written document that defines the desired opera-
                  tional environment. It answers the question: What do
                  we want to accomplish?

PURPOSE: To provide a framework for consistent decision mak-
                  ing, and to serve as a rallying point for the whole
                  company.

WHO & HOW: The executives and managers who participated in
                  first-cut education, in one or several meetings, ham-
                  mer out what the company will look like and what new
                  competitive capabilities it will have after the new
                  approach has been implemented.

TIME FRAME: One to several days.

4. COST/BENEFIT (DRP)

DEFINITION:	A written document that spells out the costs of implementation and the benefits of operating at a Class A level.
PURPOSE:	To make possible an informed decision about whether to proceed with the implementation; to build a foundation for the project; and to ensure there is buy-in and commitment from management to provide the necessary resources.
WHO & HOW:	Involves the same people and often the same meetings as the vision statement. The top person from each functional area should be accountable for providing the estimate of benefits and the eventual achievement of them.
TIME FRAME:	One day to one week.

5. PROJECT ORGANIZATION (DRP)

DEFINITION: Creation of the appropriate management and operational level team(s). Generally, this consists of a steering committee of executives and a project team of key users.

PURPOSE: To assign responsibilities and allocate people resources to the project.

WHO & HOW: Initially, much the same group as above to do the job of identifying candidates. Afterwards, certain executives and managers discuss the opportunity with the candidates to gain their acceptance of the assignment.

TIME FRAME: One day to two weeks.

6. PERFORMANCE GOALS (DRP)

DEFINITION: Agreement of what performance categories are expected to improve and what levels they are expected to reach.

PURPOSE: To identify improvements that are expected to be achieved and how they will be measured.

WHO & HOW: Essentially the same people who attended first-cut education use the knowledge gained there to set specific targets for attainment (e.g., customer delivery performance, lead time reduction, schedule compliance, cost reduction, productivity increases, inventory reductions, etc.).

TIME FRAME: One hour to one day.

Please note: In many cases it's possible for most of the activities specified in Steps 3, 4, 5, and 6 to be accomplished by the same people in the same several meetings. This is good, since there is an urgency to get started, and time is of the essence.

DRP: Distribution Resource Planning
Proven Path Detailed Implementation Plan

TASK	RESPONSIBLE	COMMENTS
1. AUDIT/ASSESSMENT I	Top Mgmt. Middle Mgmt.	Assess the company's current situation. In most cases, this is done with the help of an outside consultant with Class A credentials.
2. FIRST-CUT EDUCATION	Top Mgmt. Middle Mgmt.	What is DRP, how does it work, why should a company commit to it? Top management should attend the DRP Top Management Course, key middle managers should attend the DRP Three-Day Course.
3. VISION STATEMENT	Top Mgmt. Middle Mgmt.	A short, concise document defining what we want to accomplish, and when it should be in place.
4. COST/BENEFIT	Top Mgmt. Middle Mgmt.	A clear listing of the costs and benefits, agreed to by the key players.
A. Prepare cost/benefit.	Top Mgmt. Middle Mgmt.	Cost/benefit analysis.
B. Commit to implementation.	Top Mgmt.	Approve the implementation. Communicate the commitment. Deliver clear, consistent messages.
5. PROJECT ORGANIZATION	Top Mgmt.	Create the appropriate management and operational teams.
A. Executive Steering Committee.	Top Mgmt.	Include designation of Executive Torchbearer. Schedule review meetings once a month.
B. Project Team.	Top Mgmt.	Team Leader should be full-time. Other team members from 10 percent to 100 percent depending on their role.
C. Outside counsel.	Top Mgmt.	Outside consultant with Class A experience.
D. Spin-off task groups.	Exec. Steering Committee	Identify initial groups; more may be needed later.
6. PERFORMANCE GOALS	Top Mgmt. Middle Mgmt.	Using the ABCD Checklist, agree on expected performance levels and measurements.

7. INITIAL EDUCATION (DRP)

DEFINITION: An educational effort for all people who are involved
                 in designing and using the new tools.

PURPOSE: To provide a basic understanding of what the company
                 is striving to achieve, why it is important, and how it
                 will enable them to do their jobs more effectively.

WHO & HOW: The groups(s) selected to manage the project (Step 5)
                 must first become more knowledgeable on the ap-
                 proaches. This is usually accomplished through semi-
                 nars and internal education sessions. These people
                 would then lead the education of the larger group.
                 Business discussions led by managers and super-
                 visors, and assisted by videotapes, have proven to be a
                 practical and effective method of accomplishing this
                 step.

TIME FRAME: Throughout the implementation schedule.

8. THE SALES, LOGISTICS, AND MANUFACTURING PROCESSES (DRP)

DEFINITION: Detailed statement of how the Sales/Marketing, Logistics and Manufacturing functions will perform following implementation, and the detailed project plan necessary to achieve this.

PURPOSE: To ensure that the details of the implementation will be consistent with the vision statement; to verify that the processes that will be affected by the upcoming changes will be prioritized based on those most in need of improvement; and to create the detailed schedule necessary for effective project management.

WHO & HOW: Key people who will be directly involved lay out the detailed project schedule and, where appropriate, obtain concurrence from senior management.

TIME FRAME: One week to two months.

DRP: Distribution Resource Planning
Proven Path Detailed Implementation Plan

TASK	RESPONSIBLE	COMMENTS
7. INITIAL EDUCATION	Team Leader	Provide the necessary understanding to all people who will be designing and using the new tools.
A. Outside education for people who will be leaders at the in-house series of business meetings, and key managers.	Team Leader	To be effective discussion leaders, these managers need exposure at either the DRP Top Management Course, or the DRP Three-Day Course. The key managers mentioned here are people critical to the design or operation, but who have not been covered under first-cut education and who are not leaders for the business meetings.
B. Outside education for people designated as in-house experts.	Team Leader	Generally, in-house experts are designated in the following areas: Sales & Operations Planning, Master Production Scheduling, Purchasing, Inventory Record Accuracy, JIT/TQC, and Financial Integration. These in-house experts may or may not be part of the project team.
C. Project Team/Discussion Leaders video course.	Team Leader	A series of business meetings where the general principles are translated into the specifics of operation for your company. Acquire the DRP Video Library.
D. Top Management video course.	Executive Torchbearer/Project Leader	A series of business meetings where the top managers apply the concepts to their company.
E. Mixed Management Overview video course.	Discussion Leaders	A series of business meetings covering the overview materials, with a mixed group of managers from each of the different functional areas. The objectives are to understand the concepts, to better understand one another, and to help in team building.
F. Department specific video courses.	Discussion Leaders	Series of business meetings organized by department. The objectives are to determine specifically what changes need to be made to run the business differently in these departments. Typical groups for these meetings include, but are not limited to: Distribution Management, Traffic, Purchasing, Sales and Marketing, Finance, Management Information Systems, Personnel, and Distribution Center Employees.

DRP: Distribution Resource Planning
Proven Path Detailed Implementation Plan

TASK	RESPONSIBLE	COMMENTS
8. SALES, LOGISTICS, AND MANUFACTURING PROCESSES	Top Mgmt. Middle Mgmt.	Develop a detailed statement of how these processes will operate following implementation. The Project Team/Discussion Leaders series of business meetings (Task #7C above) generally provides most of the information needed for this task. Key issues or changes should be approved by top management. In the case of a company with their own manufacturing, this might include MRP II and/or JIT/TQC. If so, see the MRP II and JIT/TQC detailed implementation plans.

9. PLANNING AND CONTROL PROCESSES (DRP)

DEFINITION: Identification of all systems and processes necessary
               for effective planning and control, from sales & opera-
               tions planning down through detailed plant, supplier,
               and distribution schedules.

PURPOSE: To ensure that the formal planning and control systems
               either in place or to be implemented are capable of
               generating and maintaining valid plans and sched-
               ules for:

               1. Shipment of customer orders
               2. Logistics
               3. Manufacturing
               4. Purchasing
               5. Engineering
               6. Finance

WHO & HOW: The people throughout the company, in marketing and
               sales, manufacturing, purchasing, engineering, plan-
               ning, and elsewhere who will be involved in generat-
               ing plans and schedules, or in executing them. They
               do this by using their knowledge of the present oper-
               ating environment of the company with the knowledge
               they gained in initial education as to what is required.

TIME FRAME: One week to three months.

DRP: Distribution Resource Planning
Proven Path Detailed Implementation Plan

TASK	RESPONSIBLE	COMMENTS
9. PLANNING AND CONTROL PROCESSES		
A. Sales & Operations Planning.	Top Mgmt.	Identification of the systems necessary for effective planning. Some of these systems will be implemented using the pilot approach. Can be started right away. Format, policies, unit of measure, and family designations can be developed in the first few meetings and revised as needed thereafter.
B. Demand Management.	Sales Mgr.	Focus on improving the demand side of the business through sales planning, item forecasting, eliminating forecasting wherever possible by interfacing with customer scheduling systems.
C. Master Scheduling (Production or Purchase).	Logistics Mgr.	In a company with manufacturing operations, the term Master Production Scheduling is used. In a distribution operation without manufacturing, the term Purchase Schedule or Master Purchase Schedule is used. Decisions on what items will be master scheduled. Typically started with Distribution Requirements Planning as part of the pilot.
1. Develop a master scheduling policy.	Top Mgmt. Sales & Mktg. Logistics Mgr.	Should address the following: 1. Procedure for changing the master schedule (production or purchase). Who can request a change, how the proposed change is investigated, and who should approve it. 2. Periodic reviews of actual performance *vs.* the master schedule (production or purchase) with an emphasis on problem resolution.
D. Distribution Requirements Planning.	Logistics Mgr.	Begun as a pilot.

DRP: Distribution Resource Planning
Proven Path Detailed Implementation Plan

TASK	RESPONSIBLE	COMMENTS
E. Transportation Planning.	Logistics Mgr. Traffic	Sometimes implementation is delayed until after master scheduling and Distribution Requirements Planning are fully implemented.
F. Supplier Scheduling & Development.	Purchasing Mgr.	Typically started as a pilot with one or several suppliers.

10. DATA MANAGEMENT (DRP)

DEFINITION: Attaining necessary levels of data accuracy and structure, with timely reporting.

PURPOSE: To make decisions based on current, accurate information.

WHO & HOW: Accountability for data integrity must be assigned.

Data	People
Inventory Record Accuracy	Warehouse and Stockroom Personnel
Bill of Material[13] Accuracy and Structure	Product Engineering, Research and Development, Distribution
Routings (if required)	Manufacturing/Industrial Engineering

TIME FRAME: Up to several months.

---

[13] Often called formulas, recipes, practices, etc. in process flow manufacturing. In a DRP implementation, this step would refer to the distribution bill of material (i.e., which products are stocked at which locations in the distribution network).

DRP: Distribution Resource Planning
Proven Path Detailed Implementation Plan

TASK	RESPONSIBLE	COMMENTS
10. DATA MANAGEMENT		These are the steps required to attain the necessary levels of data accuracy.
A. Inventory Record Accuracy.	Distr. Center Mgrs.	Objective is a minimum 95 percent inventory record accuracy.
1. Measure a sample of items as a starting point.	Distr. Center Mgrs.	Develop an objective assessment of the starting point. Most companies use a sample of 100 items.
2. Provide the tools for limited access and transaction recording.	Distr. Center Mgrs.	Transaction system must be simple and easy to use.
3. Implement control group cycle counting.	Distr. Center Mgrs.	Used to find and fix the root causes of errors.
4. Begin cycle counting all items.	Distr. Center Mgrs.	Done after the root causes of errors have been corrected. Several approaches are commonly used: process control cycle counting, cycle counting by ABC code, random cycle counting.
B. Structure the distribution network.	Logistics Mgr.	Load bills of distribution to represent the distribution network.
C. Item Data.	Logistics Mgr. Purchasing Mgr.	The objective is to have knowledgeable people verify this information.
1. Verify order policies.	Logistics Mgr. Purchasing Mgr.	Decide between fixed-order quantity and lot-for-lot. Dynamic-order quantity calculations are not recommended. Fix the obvious errors in order quantities, use remainder as is.

DRP: Distribution Resource Planning
Proven Path Detailed Implementation Plan

TASK	RESPONSIBLE	COMMENTS
2. Verify in-transit lead times.	Logistics Mgr. Traffic Purchasing Mgr.	Use current lead times, fix the obvious errors. In the case of purchased items, work with suppliers to implement supplier scheduling to get out beyond the lead times.
3. Verify safety stock levels.	Logistics Mgr. Purchasing Mgr.	Applies to independent demand items consistent with master schedule policy. For dependent demand items, restrict to special circumstances only.

11. PROCESS IMPROVEMENT (DRP)

DEFINITION: Continuous improvement of all processes for sales, operations, logistics, and product design.

PURPOSE: To ensure survival, growth, and prosperity as a business. This is done by changing those processes that inhibit progress and/or are incompatible with the new vision.

WHO & HOW: Initially, only those people involved with the actual implementation, but eventually everyone in the company, should participate in this step. This is done by creating within the organization a deep commitment to continuing improvement, a creative discontent with the status quo.

TIME FRAME: Never ending.

DRP: Distribution Resource Planning
Proven Path Detailed Implementation Plan

TASK	RESPONSIBLE	COMMENTS
11. PROCESS IMPROVEMENT		DRP is a planning and control system. JIT/TQC is a change process; changing the business to make it more efficient, more productive, and less costly through the elimination of waste. Companies need to do both: Plan and control the business, and change their processes to continuously improve them. For the detailed implementation plan in the area of process improvement, see the JIT/TQC Detailed Implementation Plan.

12. Software Selection (DRP)

DEFINITION: Acquisition of software for planning, control, execution, analysis, and monitoring.

PURPOSE: To provide the information that supports the users in doing their jobs more effectively.

WHO & HOW: Software selection should be a joint venture involving key users as well as MIS people. This step must be accomplished relatively quickly and can be done so via the effective use of available information about manufacturing and distribution software. (For more information, see *The Standard System,* 1989 Oliver Wight Limited Publications, Inc.).

TIME FRAME: Several days to several weeks.

DRP: Distribution Resource Planning
Proven Path Detailed Implementation Plan

TASK	RESPONSIBLE	COMMENTS
12. SOFTWARE		
A. Select software.	MIS Mgr.	Select and implement the software to support the planning and control systems identified above.
	MIS Mgr. Logistics Mgr.	Select software that meets most of the needs from a user and MIS point of view.
1. Acquire *The Standard System* book.	MIS Mgr. Logistics Mgr.	Available from Oliver Wight Limited Publications, this book provides an explanation of what a typical software package should provide.
2. If needed, schedule software consulting audit.	MIS Mgr. Logistics Mgr.	Helpful in situations where new software is being used or extensive modification and/or interfacing is required.
B. Evaluate systems work and acquire necessary resources.	MIS Mgr.	Includes work needed for modifications, interfacing, and temporary bridges.
C. Implement necessary modules with modifications and interfacing.	MIS Mgr.	Typical modules include: Inventory Transactions, Bills of Material, Master Scheduling (Production or Purchase), Distribution Requirements Planning, Transportation Planning, Purchasing, Financial Integration.
D. Agree on MIS performance standards.	MIS Mgr. Logistics Mgr.	Response times, on-time completion of planning run, reports, etc.

123

13. PILOT AND CUTOVER (DRP)[14]

DEFINITION: Conversion of the current process to the new process.

PURPOSE: To prove that the new tool actually works and to begin to benefit from it.

WHO & HOW: The people directly involved with the implementation begin to operate their part of the business using the new systems and/or processes.

TIME FRAME: Several weeks to several months.

---

[14] Cutover applies only to company-wide implementations. It entails adding the rest of the products/items onto the system following a successful operation of the pilot.

DRP: Distribution Resource Planning
Proven Path Detailed Implementation Plan

TASK	RESPONSIBLE	COMMENTS
13. PILOT AND CUTOVER	Team Leader Project Team Logistics Mgr. Involved Users	Conversion of the current processes to the new processes using a pilot approach.
A. Complete three pilots.	Team Leader Project Team Involved Users	Pilots are: 1. Computer pilot to test the software. 2. Conference room pilot to test procedures and people's understanding. 3. Live pilot to test the new processes and verify they are working. Systems that are typically implemented using the pilot approach are: 1. Master Scheduling (Production or Purchase). 2. Distribution Requirements Planning. 3. Supplier Scheduling and Development.
B. Monitor critical measurements.	Team Leader	Before moving into cutover, verify that the new processes and systems are working.
C. Group remaining products into several groups.	Logistics Mgr.	Three or four groups are typical.
D. Bring each group onto the new systems.	Logistics Mgr. Involved Users	Each group will require intense planner coverage to get them settled down.

14. Performance Measurements (DRP)

DEFINITION: Comparison of actual results to previously established
                 key performance variables.

PURPOSE: To verify that the changes are delivering the expected
                 results, and to provide feedback for implementation
                 corrections.

WHO & HOW: This step should be done by people directly involved
                 in the implementation, perhaps with assistance from
                 other departments, such as MIS, accounting, etc.

TIME FRAME: Duration of the pilot and/or cutover phase.

15. AUDIT ASSESSMENT II (DRP)

DEFINITION: Analysis of the company's situation, problems, and opportunities in light of the newly implemented tool(s).

PURPOSE: To verify the effectiveness of the newly implemented tools, and to define the next steps on the continuing improvement journey.

This is another critically important step. Under no circumstances should it be skipped, since one of its missions is to define the next improvement initiative to follow. Should this step be omitted, the company's drive for operational excellence will stall out, and the company will be left in a competitively vulnerable position.

WHO & HOW: Participants in this step include the executives, a wide range of operating managers, and, in virtually all cases, outside consultants with Class A credentials in MRP II, JIT/TQC, and/or DRP.

The process is one of fact finding, identifying areas of consensus and disagreement, matching the company's current status and strategies with the tools it has available for execution. The end result should be the development of an action plan to move the company onto a path of continuous improvement.

TIME FRAME: One week to one month.

16. Ongoing Education (DRP)

Definition: A continuing effort to upgrade everyone's awareness
                and skills.

Purpose: To emphasize the importance of people's jobs and to
                increase their abilities to do them. Ongoing education
                reinforces initial education as well as being necessary
                for new employees and employees in new jobs.

Who & How: Department managers and supervisors are responsible
                for helping their people grow. Aids, such as video-
                tapes, contribute to the effectiveness of the education
                program.

Time Frame: Forever.

DRP: Distribution Resource Planning
Proven Path Detailed Implementation Plan

TASK	RESPONSIBLE	COMMENTS
14. PERFORMANCE MEASUREMENTS	Dept. Heads	Compare actual results to the previously agreed-upon key measurements. Typical performance measurements include: 1. Production Plan (or Open To Buy) performance. 2. Master Schedule (Production or Purchase) performance. 3. Supplier Delivery performance. Other measurements include: 1. Customer Service. 2. Cost.
15. AUDIT/ASSESSMENT II	Top Mgmt. Middle Mgmt.	Re-assess the company's situation. Where are the current opportunities, what needs to be done next. This could be a phase 2 of the implementation, a concentrated effort to improve current levels of performance, etc. In most cases, this is done with the help of an outside consultant with Class A credentials.
16. ONGOING EDUCATION	Dept. Heads	Run a continuing program of outside education and business meetings to improve skill levels and company operating results.
A. Educate key managers new to the business.	Top Mgmt.	New managers in key positions need exposure at either the DRP Top Management Course or the DRP Three-Day Course to continue achieving full operating benefits.
B. Maintain in-house experts.	Dept. Heads	Also important to continue achieving full operating benefits.
C. Continue the series of business meetings.	Dept. Heads	These meetings focus on how to improve the operating results of the business through the use of these tools. It's good to stand back and look at the situation from time to time. Sometimes new people are run through a special series of meetings; more typically, they are included into the ongoing series of business meetings.

Although some steps can be done quickly, while others require considerable time, it is essential to complete each step if the full potential of MRP II, JIT/TQC, and DRP is to be attained. Nevertheless, general managers who confront major problems are often anxious to achieve improvements, and may not insist on a vision statement, a cost/benefit analysis, or a description of the new sales, logistics, and manufacturing processes. These executives need to resist the temptation to minimize the importance of the 16 steps—the success of the company's goals are tied directly to how well each activity is carried out.

Now, keeping the generalized Proven Path in mind, let's look at the Fast-Track Implementation approaches.

Fast-Track Implementation

The Proven Path represents an evolutionary step, albeit a major one, rather than a radical departure. But it also opens the way for an important and exciting new development: Fast-Track Implementation.

Just-In-Time (JIT), as we said earlier, is best implemented via a series of small pieces. We call this approach the Breakthrough JIT Pilot. Breakthrough JIT focuses on a narrow band of the manufacturing operation, enabling a company to have a JIT pilot[15] up and running within 100 days of the start of implementation. This means attaining visible results in terms of reduced lead times, improved quality, and reduced inventory.

Many times our associates have effectively utilized the same Fast-Track Implementation approach for both MRP II and DRP, and these are referred to as Quick-Slice MRP and Fail-Safe Mini-DRP.

Quick-Slice MRP enables a company to achieve substantial MRP-generated benefits that are visible on the plant floor and financial statements within three to six months. The goal of Quick-Slice MRP is to provide quick results, rather than realizing payback in 12 to 18 months as in the traditional company-wide implementation approach.

---

[15] In Fast-Track Implementation, the word "pilot" has a specific meaning: It generates significant operational benefits. In an across-the-board implementation, the pilot refers to a live test of certain processes and systems intended to prove out the new approach, not necessarily to generate operational benefits.

131

Fail-Safe Mini-DRP enables companies to achieve the benefits of DRP within a small segment of the business—quickly and with minimal disruption to existing operations—in a similar time frame of three to six months.

Let's look at each of these Fast-Track Implementation approaches in more detail.

Fast-Track Implementation—The Breakthrough JIT Pilot

The Breakthrough JIT pilot approach is a high-yield/low-risk implementation process developed during years of hands-on experience and continually reconfirmed by successful results across a wide range of companies and industries. It is designed to help companies safely and economically achieve the breakthrough results made possible by JIT/TQC.

The difficult changes and pitfalls to continuous improvement are addressed up front when the interest is highest and the scope of the change is manageable. There is a marketing strategy behind the Breakthrough JIT pilot implementation approach as well. The initial successes are designed to make it obvious that the only logical course of action is to continue. This implementation approach is designed to create a model of the future. It enables companies to continuously improve their ability to economically respond to change, by yielding ten-fold results, not simply 10-percent improvements! A pilot approach is used to maximize the knowledge gained, keep the effort manageable, the risk low, and the progress rapid.

IMPLEMENTATION ELEMENTS

The Breakthrough JIT implementation approach follows the Proven Path methodology, using the same steps shown in Figure 1: audit/assessment I, first-cut education, cost/benefit analysis, etc. For detailed information on how to structure the JIT/TQC pilot, see *Just-in-Time: Making it Happen* (1989 Oliver Wight Limited Publications, Inc.). Here, we'll simply highlight a few of the significant areas.

Implementation Team

Usually the seeds of JIT/TQC first develop in manufacturing, but quickly we see that constraints to responsiveness exist throughout the company, not just in manufacturing. Because JIT/TQC will affect the entire company, it is essential to obtain support from all functional areas for the breakthrough pilot.

As will be evident when examining the pilot criteria, the Breakthrough JIT pilot implementation team should consist of a small group of key people from manufacturing and related departments. Although support is needed, participation on the JIT implementation team by every functional area is not essential initially. Those areas that are not on the critical implementation path can elect to wait. For example, changes will occur in accounts payable, but not typically to any large degree during the pilot. Therefore, accounts payable can wait to begin active participation in the changes if they prefer to do so. The same may be true for marketing and design. To progress past the pilot stage and achieve a breakthrough for the entire company, the effort will eventually require active participation by all areas.

Breakthrough JIT Pilot Specifications

The pilot selected should be a product line or a major operational area. It should contain three or more manufacturing customer/supplier relationships (e.g., three separate shops involved in the production of a product line, or three major areas of one large shop producing items for many products). The size of the pilot must be such that people can feel the rhythm of the JIT/TQC pull process, and experience how it can strengthen customer/supplier relations. But the size should be large enough that management will notice the results, and see when they need to respond with help when problems are encountered. Finally, it should be of a size that will maximize what we learn, while small enough to avoid spreading resources too thin.

Let's look at what the JIT/TQC pilot will look like when it goes "on the air." Typical changes[16] include:

- Kanban[17] techniques will be used.
- Work orders will be eliminated.
- Labor will be collected by exception.
- Material will be stored at the point of use.
- JIT's "one less at a time" process will be used to prioritize and stimulate action to eliminate constraints to improved responsiveness.
- TQC's plan/do/check/action process will be used to eliminate the root cause of constraints exposed by JIT.

The kanban technique makes the JIT "one less at a time" process practical. Kanbans are what we remove. They allow for formal, but visual, control of the flow through each process by those closest to the operations—the operators. Visual controls also make possible rapid identification of problem areas. In addition, kanbans physically connect customers and suppliers together; they stimulate communications and provide team-building opportunities for the resolution of joint problems.

As the "one less at a time" process of JIT begins, constraints will be exposed. The Breakthrough JIT pilot specifications require the minimum pilot team (and later everyone) not only to learn how to expose constraints using the JIT process, but also to learn how to resolve them using the TQC process. Therefore, the serious education and application of TQC's plan/do/check/action process should be in place.

---

[16] Some of these criteria may need to be temporarily modified in certain government-regulated industries (e.g., defense, pharmaceuticals, etc.).

[17] A method for JIT production in which downstream operations pull from feeding operations upstream. Feeding operations are authorized to produce only after receiving a kanban trigger from the consuming operation downstream. Kanban in Japanese loosely translated means card or signal, and is pronounced "kahn-bahn."

IMPLEMENTATION TIMETABLE

The time from when the implementation team attends a detailed implementation class until the pilot is "on the air" should not exceed 120 days, and frequently can be done faster. There is considerable work to do, but not so much that more time is necessary. If more time is scheduled, the project of implementing the JIT/TQC process will certainly expand to fill the allotment. The more time that is used, the greater the chance the company will lose the opportunity for change. The company will be reorganized, too busy, and therefore the process will be too slow. When the "window of opportunity" to change opens, capitalize on it before it closes.

Remember, this is a pilot. The goal is to practice continuous improvement, which means all the answers won't be available. Keep it simple and flexible—not everything needs to be computerized and as elegant as it will be in the final form. But do get started, practice, and learn.

Implementing JIT/TQC is much like learning to ride a bicycle. Knowledge of how it works is important, and selecting a logical location to practice is wise. But reading books, watching videotapes, and talking isn't enough—people never really understand something until they try it. Having a little help at first is a smart idea—someone who has ridden a bicycle before can share experiences, teach the proper techniques, and steer away from potential problem areas. But eventually it's time to get on the bicycle. It can be a little scary and it's possible to get a bit bruised, but practice makes perfect. Or, in the case of JIT/TQC, practice yields continual improvement.

CONCLUSION

There are probably as many possible strategies to implement JIT/TQC as there are people wishing they had more competitive processes. No other approach, however, delivers the order of magnitude of results as fast, as consistently, and as inexpensively as does the Breakthrough JIT pilot approach. It is not easy, but for those that are serious about competing, it delivers.

Fast-Track Implementation— Quick-Slice MRP

To implement MRP II throughout the company, many things must be done: All the people must be educated; all the data must be loaded and kept accurate; all master schedule items must be managed; all the software must be selected, installed, and interfaced; etc. This amount of work is seldom challenged. Additionally, the upper limit in time has been 24 months. If all these things could not be done, it was recommended that the implementation resources be increased. That is, "Never change the schedule; never change the load; simply add more horse."

This may not always be possible. In fact, even when possible, it may not always be desirable.

As we've just seen, JIT is implemented in pilot form using a product or process. It's a strategically selected piece of the whole that is converted over to JIT. Its aim is not only to prove the process, but to generate real results on the plant floor and elsewhere in the company. This pilot approach makes a lot of sense. It's another version of "eating the elephant a bite at a time."

137

Quick-Slice MRP is the JIT implementation approach applied to MRP II. It involves:

1. Selecting a "pareto"[18] high-impact product line—a very important slice of the business.

2. Implementing as many of the MRP II functions as possible for that product.

3. Completing the pilot in a very short time.

Hence the label "Quick-Slice MRP."

WHERE QUICK-SLICE MRP APPLIES

There are seven distinct situations in which Quick-Slice MRP makes sense.

Situation 1, "JIT Without MRP II": The company is implementing JIT and does not have an MRP II system. And while it is desirable and logical to bring up MRP and JIT at the same time, the combined effort strains resources. Quick-Slice MRP allows for proper planning without slowing down the JIT implementation. For companies implementing JIT and MRP at the same time, Quick-Slice MRP is the only realistic opportunity they have. Obviously, in this situation, the JIT pilot and the Quick-Slice MRP would be done on the same products.

Situation 2, "Quick Payback": Senior management understands MRP II well, but wants a quick payback for operating reasons. This could be a company with new management that wants to make their mark quickly and decisively.

Situation 3, "Jumbo-Size Company": The large size of the company may make a standard implementation unwieldy. Large implementations tend to be more difficult than small ones. The first Quick-Slice MRP

---

[18] Pareto's Law refers to the principle of the "vital few - trivial many." For example, in many companies thirty to sixty percent of their sales come from five to ten percent of their products. Pareto's Law is also the basis for ABC inventory analysis.

implementation would be followed by another, and another, so that enthusiasm, momentum, and progress is kept at its peak.

Situation 4, "Middle Up": Middle management understands the need for a better planning and scheduling system. Top management, however, does not perceive the need, nor is it receptive to financing a major MRP II effort. In this case there is no real chance of achieving Class A, if a company-wide implementation were pursued. The benefit of the Quick-Slice MRP approach lies in its ability to create heroes quickly and allow success to breed more success.

Situation 5, "Bleeding from the Neck": The company is in dire financial straits and needs help quickly. The advantages of Quick-Slice MRP are focus and time. It can be done for a product line and perhaps generate cash through inventory reductions, while improving on time deliveries to the customers.

Situation 6, "Creaking Systems": The company has a marginal MRP system. Data-processing people champion the project, and the chances are high that a re-implementation will in reality end up being a re-installation of software. Quick-Slice MRP, in this environment, can quickly demonstrate that people are really the difference between success and disappointing results.

Situation 7, "We're Unique": The company is pioneering in their industry; they can't find another company with a similar process that has been successful with MRP II. Management is reluctant to invest heavily in MRP II until they can see it handling the company's particular problem. Quick-Slice MRP gives management the opportunity to do this quickly and with very little cost.

IMPLEMENTING QUICK-SLICE MRP

With Quick-Slice MRP, the resources and time are fixed, but the amount of work is adjusted to accommodate them. Time is the ultimate enemy. The longer the implementation takes, the more it will cost and the greater the "window of risk." Thus, the implementation should be in weeks or months, not years. If an implementation is to be done quickly, the number of people performing it must be minimized. A task force of three or four people is preferable to a project team of a dozen or more. If the time is set at eight weeks and the task force is limited to four people, the variable is the amount of work that can be accomplished. How much of an MRP II system can be made operational with this resource in this time frame? Obviously not very much. Properly selected, however, it can have a major impact on the business.

The only things in manufacturing that really count are product performance, quality, cost, and service. If the task force does not positively affect one or more of these areas, it is not contributing to the company's competitive position. Creating and maintaining 95-percent inventory record accuracy is a major milestone in attaining Class A MRP II. But 95-percent record accuracy does not make for corporate heroes. On the other hand, improving delivery performance on a major product line generates accolades of the highest order. Thus, when determining what and how much work is to be done by the task force, it should be calculated with a competitive position in mind.

THE METHODOLOGY

The methodology behind Quick-Slice MRP is really *focus*. Once the slice has been selected, its critical elements are addressed quickly and with maximum effectiveness. The four major divisions of The Oliver Wight Companies ABCD Checklist provide a vehicle for discussing this point. These areas are:

1. Planning and Control

2. Data Management

3. Process Improvement

4. Performance Measurements

An additional area of consideration is software.

PLANNING AND CONTROL

There are six elements that comprise the planning and control category:

1. *Sales & Operations Planning:* Although only one product or product family may be included in the slice, it is imperative that sales & operations planning be done on all product families. This is a quick, straightforward senior management responsibility. Sales & operations planning allows top management to set the tempo of the company and orchestrate its success. They should be able to begin this process and have it operational within 60 days from start.

   Note: To be successful with sales & operations planning, experience has shown that MRP II education is mandatory for all participants in this process. Most of these people will have been so educated in the first-cut education phase. Those who have not need education immediately.

2. *Rough-Cut Capacity Planning:* As an adjunct to sales & operations planning, rough-cut capacity planning should start at the same time. Like sales & operations planning, rough-cut capacity planning should be done on all products and work centers, not just the slice. Rough-cut capacity planning should become operational between the first and second sales & operations planning meeting—within 45 days from start.

3. *Demand Management:* The marketing and sales departments need to put extra efforts into forecasting the anticipated sales of the slice product. Typical instructions might be, "We realize you have a lot of work to do on a day-to-day basis, but review the slice product continuously. If something has to slip, don't let it be your forecasts of slice sales. The more visibility you can give us, the better service we can give you." It's critical that marketing and sales put the extra effort into improving and monitoring the forecast of the slice.

4. *Master Scheduling:* Of all the aspects of Quick- Slice MRP, master scheduling is probably the simplest. Since only one product or product family is to be master scheduled, the scheduling department should dedicate the necessary amount of time to do it properly. If this

appears to be a major problem, then the slice should be re-examined. It is particularly attractive to have the ability to calculate "available to promise," even if it is done manually. This is part of the payback to the sales and marketing departments for their extra efforts in forecasting the slice business. It will assist the sales department in promising customer orders.

5. *Material Requirements Planning:* Material planning is done using MRP, but only on the parts included in the slice. Nuts, bolts, lock washers, and other low-cost parts should be avoided. If they are presently being planned on an order point system, they should initially remain that way. Where the slice has common parts with other products, an independent demand needs to be entered to accommodate those products that will not be planned on MRP (i.e., nonslice parts).

6. *Manufacturing and Purchasing Schedules:* Complexity at this level should be avoided. The main thrust here is to communicate to the factory and purchasing what is needed and when. This, of course, only applies to the items included in the slice. A simple open-order listing, handwritten if necessary, may be all that is required. (This may sound simplistic, but don't forget that today's shortage list tells the production supervisors and buyers the same information—only not nearly as well.) If kanban can be incorporated in some of the manufacturing processes, it makes operational scheduling particularly easy. In these situations, the master schedule and MRP for the buyers are the key schedules.

The problem of relative priorities—how slice and nonslice parts are scheduled when they go through the same work center—tends to cause some confusion. The slice parts are planned by MPS and MRP, while nonslice parts are not. In each case, the production supervisor or scheduler must do the reconciliation. They should, however, be driven by the fact that the slice parts have valid due dates and nonslice parts have dubious due dates. Simply put, they should meet the due dates of the slice parts as a top-priority task.

DATA MANAGEMENT

Inventory record accuracy, bills of material accuracy and structure, and item analysis should be limited to those included in the slice. Special efforts may be required. For instance, if inventory record accuracy is a problem and limited access is required, it may be necessary to segregate the slice components and raw materials and sequester them in a special stockroom. The same holds true for the bills of material. Since only the slice product and its components are going to be planned and controlled using MPS and MRP, they are the only ones that need to have their bills of material restructured and purged of errors.

Since the slice is limited by time and resources, the number of bills, item master files, and inventory records can all be made ready by design. Again, it must be emphasized that time is the enemy. Whatever needs to be done to prepare and load this data must be done within the implementation schedule. Sometimes this means things like manually loading data, creating limited access within only a portion of the storeroom, and using handwritten procedures. It may not be pretty, but it can produce dramatic progress.

PROCESS IMPROVEMENT

Flow shops are much easier to plan and schedule than are job shops.[19] Thus, if possible, create flow within the sliced product's manufacturing process. This may take the form of placing equipment in cells by physically moving them or by "celling" them using kanban. Whichever approach is used, the results need to be reflected in flattening the bills of material, changing the information in the item master file, and, where applicable, shortening the routings.

---

[19] The job-shop form of organization is one where the resources (equipment, people skills) are grouped by like type. Example: a machine shop. A flow shop has dissimilar equipment and/or skills located next to one another, based on what they do to the product. Example: a filling/packaging line in a food processing plant. Another example: a manufacturing cell.

PERFORMANCE MEASUREMENTS

Most operational performance measurements that apply to a Class A MRP II company-wide implementation also apply to a Quick-Slice MRP:

- Production planning performance $+/-2$ percent.

- Master schedule performance 95- to 100 percent on the slice products.

- Plant schedule performance 95- to 100 percent on the slice components.

- Supplier delivery performance 95- to 100 percent on those slice components being vendor scheduled.[20]

These are overview performance measurements, and are supported in more detail in The Oliver Wight Companies ABCD Checklist. As you apply the measurements, bear in mind that Quick-Slice MRP is not a test; rather, it is a first step applied across a slice of the business. It should be operated for maximum operational benefit—visible on the plant floor, in customer service, and in the financial statements.

SOFTWARE

Today, MPS/MRP software is available for personal computers costing only a few thousand dollars and capable of handling many thousands of items. These are more than adequate to run the slice. The critical issue here is to buy the software quickly and get on with the implementation. A major pitfall is detailed research on software. Clearly, it is possible to spend more time on selecting the software than on implementing the slice. Therefore, the best approach by far is to pick a package quickly and run with it. If a choice cannot be made between two packages, flip a coin. Time is the enemy.

Once the slice is up and running and you've decided to pursue a

---

[20] Vendor scheduling is a technique by which a company provides its suppliers with time-phased forward-looking schedules, generated by MRP, rather than individual hardcopy purchase orders.

complete MRP II implementation, a more complete and functional software package would most likely be selected. And there's good news for companies that already have MRP II software on their computer: Forget about buying micro-computer software; use what you already have, provided this can be done quickly and easily.

Whichever approach is applicable, the Quick-Slice MRP implementation team needs to concentrate on the people, data, and software in that order of priority.

CONCLUSION

Quick-Slice MRP is a legitimate cross between the traditional MRP II implementation and JIT implementation methodology. It is clearly different than the traditional approach, and offers true advantages. Already tried and proven, we believe it will become the most common and accepted method of implementing MRP II in the near future. It is a major breakthrough.

Quick-Slice Detailed Implementation Plan

The following pages list the detailed implementation for Quick-Slice MRP. This plan is a modified version of the MRP II Detailed Implementation Plan, altered to eliminate tasks that would not be part of a Quick-Slice implementation. For example, the large education program that would be part of a full implementation has been cut back to an education program for the project team charged with the responsibility for implementing the slice.

In other cases, the tasks remain the same, but the amount of work is significantly reduced because they happen only for the slice items. For example, inventory record accuracy would still have to be attained, but only on the items in the slice. In fact, the implementation plan for Quick-Slice is not much smaller than the implementation plan for a company-wide MRP II implementation. However, the work required to implement Quick-Slice is significantly less, and the time required is only a few months.

There are a number of abbreviations used in the RESPONSIBLE

column of the detailed implementation plans. The table below shows these abbreviations and their meaning:

Dept.	Department
Distr.	Distribution
Engr.	Engineering (either Design or Manufacturing)
Exec.	Executive
Mgmt.	Management
Mgr.	Manager
MIS	Management Information Systems
P&IC	Production & Inventory Control
Suprvsn.	Supervision

Quick-Slice MRP
Proven Path Detailed Implementation Plan

TASK	RESPONSIBLE	COMMENTS
1. AUDIT/ASSESSMENT I	Top Mgmt. Middle Mgmt.	Assess the company's current situation. In most cases, this is done with the help of an outside consultant with Class A credentials.
2. FIRST-CUT EDUCATION	Top Mgmt. Middle Mgmt.	What is MRP II, how does it work, why should a company commit to it? Top management should attend the Top Management Course, key middle managers should attend the Five Day Course, Executive Torchbearer and Team Leader should attend Successful Implementation Class.
3. VISION STATEMENT	Top Mgmt. Middle Mgmt.	A short, concise document defining what we want to accomplish, and when it should be in place.
4. COST/BENEFIT	Top Mgmt. Middle Mgmt.	A quick listing of the costs and benefits as applied to the slice only.
5. PROJECT ORGANIZATION	Top Mgmt.	Create the appropriate management and operational teams to implement the slice.
A. Executive Steering Committee.	Top Mgmt.	Include designation of Executive Torchbearer. Schedule review meetings once a month.
B. Project Team.	Top Mgmt.	Team Leader should be full-time.
C. Outside counsel.	Top Mgmt.	Outside consultant with Class A experience.
6. PERFORMANCE GOALS	Top Mgmt. Middle Mgmt.	Using the ABCD Checklist, agree on expected performance levels and measurements.
7. INITIAL EDUCATION	Team Leader	Provide the necessary understanding to the team members who will be designing and implementing the slice.
A. Outside education for team members.	Team Leader	To be effective team members, these people need exposure at the Five Day Course.

Quick-Slice MRP
Proven Path Detailed Implementation Plan

TASK	RESPONSIBLE	COMMENTS
B. Project Team video course.	Team Leader	A series of business meetings where the general principles are translated into the specifics of operation (for the slice only). Acquire the MRP II Video Library.
8. SALES, LOGISTICS, AND MANUFACTURING PROCESSES	Top Mgmt. Middle Mgmt.	Develop a detailed statement of how these processes will operate following implementation (for the slice only). The Project Team/ Discussion Leaders series of business meetings (Task #7B above) generally provides most of the information needed for this task.
9. PLANNING AND CONTROL PROCESSES		Identification of the systems necessary for effective planning (slice only). Some of these systems will be implemented using the pilot approach.
A. Sales & Operations Planning.	Top Mgmt.	Start for all items, not just slice product(s). Format, policies, unit of measure, and family designations can be developed in the first few meetings and revised as needed thereafter.
B. Demand Management.	Sales Mgr.	Slice items only.
C. Master Production Scheduling.	P&IC Mg.	Slice items only.
1. Develop a master scheduling policy.	Top Mgmt. Sales & Mktg. P&IC Mgr. Mfg. Supervsn.	Should address the following: 1. Procedure for changing the master production schedule. Who can request a change, how the proposed change is investigated, and who should approve it. 2. Periodic reviews of actual production vs. the master production schedule with an emphasis on problem resolution.
D. Material Planning.	P&IC Mgr.	Slice items only. Begun as a pilot.
E. Shop Scheduling.	P&IC Mgr. Mfg. Supervsn.	Slice items only, simple shop schedules.
F. Supplier Scheduling & Development	Purchasing Mgr.	Slice items only, simple supplier schedules.

150

Quick-Slice MRP
Proven Path Detailed Implementation Plan

TASK	RESPONSIBLE	COMMENTS
10. DATA MANAGEMENT		These are the steps required to attain the necessary levels of data accuracy (slice items only).
A. Inventory Record Accuracy.	Stockroom Mgr.	Objective is a minimum 95 percent inventory record accuracy (slice items only).
1. Provide the tools for limited access and transaction recording.	Stockroom Mgr.	It may be necessary to physically isolate the items in the slice. Transaction system must be simple and easy to use.
2. Implement control-group cycle counting.	Stockroom Mgr.	Used to find and fix the causes of errors.
3. Inventory all slice items.	Stockroom Mgr.	Done to bring the accuracy of all slice items to a minimum of 95 percent. May have to be done several times to keep the accuracy at least 95 percent if the causes of errors have not been corrected.
B. Bill of Material Accuracy.	Engineering Mgr.	Objective is a minimum 98 percent bill of material accuracy, and an accurate bill of material structure (slice items only).
1. Verify bills of material for correct item numbers and quantity per.	Engineering Mgr.	Typically done by exception: issue to manufacturing per the bill of material and track exceptions. A line-by-line audit and disassembly of the product can also be used where appropriate. Objective is to highlight errors and correct them.
2. Verify correct structure in the bills of material.	Engineering Mgr.	Typical areas of work include: 1. Representing how material moves in the factory. 2. Showing raw material on the bills of material. 3. Including modules and self-consumed assemblies where appropriate. 4. Removing unnecessary levels from the bills of material.

151

Quick-Slice MRP
Proven Path Detailed Implementation Plan

TASK	RESPONSIBLE	COMMENTS
C. Item Data.	P&IC Mgr. Purchasing Mgr.	Have knowledgeable people verify this information (slice items only).
1. Verify order policies.	P&IC Mgr. Purchasing Mgr.	Fix the obvious errors in order quantities, use remainder as is.
2. Verify lead times.	P&IC Mgr. Purchasing Mgr.	Manufactured items: use simple consistent scheduling rules, fix the obvious problems. Purchased items: use current lead times, fix the obvious problems.
3. Verify safety stock levels.	P&IC Mgr. Purchasing Mgr.	Applies to independent demand items consistent with master schedule policy. For dependent demand items, restrict to special circumstances only.
11. PROCESS IMPROVEMENT		If a flow shop can be created quickly to replace a job shop, this will make it easier to plan and schedule.
A. Identify JIT activities.	Top Mgmt. Middle Mgmt. Mfg. Supervsn.	Activities like: cells, kanban, and reducing levels in the bills of material for the slice items.
B. Implementation of JIT activities identified above.	Execution Teams	Each team is measured against their charter and individual implementation plan. For more details, see the JIT/TQC Detailed Implementation Plan.
12. SOFTWARE	MIS Mgr.	Select and implement the software to support the slice items. This may be temporary software (like a PC-based software package) or the current software if it is already up and running.
A. Select software.	MIS Mgr. P&IC Mfg. Supervsn.	A quick selection is essential here. In the case of "temporary" software, this can with a minimum of evaluation.

Quick-Slice MRP
Proven Path Detailed Implementation Plan

TASK	RESPONSIBLE	COMMENTS
1. Acquire *The Standard System* book.	MIS Mgr. P&IC Mfg. Supervsn.	Available from Oliver Wight Limited Publications, this book provides an explanation of what a typical software package should provide.
B. Implement necessary modules.	MIS Mgr.	This should be done with little, if any, interfacing of systems. Typical modules include: Inventory Transactions, Bills of Material, Master Production Scheduling, Material Requirements Planning.
13. PILOT AND CUTOVER	Team Members	Typically, there is no pilot in a Quick-Slice implementation. All the slice items are brought up on the system at once. However, the following implementation steps for a pilot are still appropriate for the implementation of the slice items.
A. Complete three pilots.	Team Members	Pilots are: 1. Computer pilot to test the software. 2. Conference room pilot to test procedures and people's understanding. 3. Live pilot (or, in this case, slice implementation) to test the new processes and verify they are working.
14. PERFORMANCE MEASUREMENTS	Team Members	Compare actual results to the previously agreed-upon key measurements. Typical performance measurements include: 1. Production Plan performance. 2. Master Production Schedule performance. 3. Manufacturing Schedule performance. 4. Supplier Delivery performance.
15. AUDIT/ASSESSMENT II	Top Mgmt. Middle Mgmt.	Re-assess the company's situation. Is it now time to implement MRP II across all items? What's next?
16. ONGOING EDUCATION		In the case of Quick Slice, ongoing education typically means initial education for the next phase of implementation.

153

Fast-Track Implementation— Fail-Safe Mini-DRP

Distribution Resource Planning (DRP) has been in existence since 1975, and is now accepted as the standard method of managing and controlling distribution operations. Many companies recognize that integrating the needs of distribution with the capabilities of manufacturing can best be accomplished using DRP. Since 1984, DRP has also become recognized as a valuable tool for retailers, wholesalers, and distributors.

Despite the impressive results that can be obtained with DRP, only one company in ten has heard of the technique or has actually done something with it. One of the reasons for this is that executives often cannot wait the 12 to 18 months it takes to implement DRP, and they balk at the $250,000 to $500,000 cost associated with a full-scale DRP implementation. Fail-Safe Mini-DRP was created to fill the breach, by helping companies quickly experience the benefits of DRP on a limited scale. Once the company enjoys the dramatic results that inevitably accompany Fail-Safe Mini-DRP, it's much easier to get top management to commit the resources necessary for a full-scale implementation.

WHERE FAIL-SAFE MINI-DRP APPLIES

Situation 1, "Bleeding from the Neck": Top management says, "We can't wait—we're taking on water." Fail-Safe Mini-DRP yields impressive payback in a matter of weeks.

Situation 2, "Jumbo-size Company": DRP is too big—how do we swallow the whole thing? Performing a pilot on a product or product line, followed by a second pilot, enables the company to proceed with small, digestible chunks.

Situation 3, "Middle Up": Top management isn't convinced—does DRP really work? Fail-Safe Mini-DRP provides very quick validation of the program.

Situation 4, "We're Unique": People believe their company requires unique solutions. Fail-Safe Mini-DRP shows them that DRP works for them as well as any other kind of company.

THE COMPONENTS OF FAIL-SAFE MINI-DRP

Fail-Safe Mini-DRP entails using DRP to manage a limited number of high-impact products. It can be implemented in about three months and costs only 5-to 10 percent of an average full- scale implementation. As with the other two Fast-Track Implementation approaches (Quick-Slice MRP and Breakthrough JIT), Fail-Safe Mini-DRP follows the Proven Path implementation route. Several of the steps deserve special emphasis:

Audit/Assessment I

This evaluation is conducted to determine where the company is today and what it must do to successfully implement DRP. This phase eliminates the risk of a false start. It provides all necessary elements needed to arrive at a "go/no go" decision.

Software

The Fail-Safe Mini-DRP project almost always involves low-cost, easy-to-use, micro-based software. This is because, unlike those using MRP II, relatively few companies already have mainframe or minicomputer software for DRP. These high-quality, PC-based software packages exist today, and they're fully capable of supporting a Fail-Safe Mini-DRP implementation. They can be purchased for less than $10,000.

The key issue is not which software package to select; rather a decision must be made quickly and the implementation must move on if Fail-Safe is to succeed. Once Fail-Safe Mini-DRP is operational and the company decides on a full-scale DRP implementation, a minicomputer or mainframe software package may have to be selected. The experience gained during the Fail-Safe implementation will give the company valuable insights into making a better permanent software selection.

THE METHODOLOGY

The methodology for Fail-Safe Mini-DRP has been developed from the Oliver Wight Companies ABCD Checklist, which has four major groupings that are used to measure the effectiveness and performance of a company having a sales, distribution, and manufacturing process. These groupings include:

- Planning and Control
- Data Management
- Process Improvement
- Performance Measurements

PLANNING AND CONTROL

Planning and controlling resources in a logistics organization is concerned with deploying people and equipment, material, space, transportation, inventory investment, etc. A number planning sequences must be

performed depending on whether you're a retailer/wholesaler or a manufacturer:

Sales and Purchase Planning (for Retail/Wholesale): Although only one
product or product group may be included in Fail-Safe Mini-DRP, it is
mandatory to carry out sales and purchase planning on all product
groups. Top management must be responsible for this action, to formal-
ize the high level planning process and link it with other management
levels within the organization. The sales and purchase planning process
should become operational within 60 days from the start of the Fail-Safe
Mini-DRP implementation.

Sales & Operations Planning (for Manufacturers): The sales & operations planning process must be institutionalized across all product lines
even though only one product or one product line may be included in the
Fail-Safe Mini-DRP implementation.

Demand Management: Companies need to provide sales forecasts for
the Fail-Safe Mini-DRP products. These forecasts must then be spread
across distribution centers (DCs) that stock the product. This spreading
function is usually done by someone other than marketing and sales.
The important point is that the sum of the DC forecasts must add up to
marketing's forecast. Extra effort is necessary on the part of marketing
and sales to improve and monitor forecasts for products in the Fail-Safe
Mini-DRP program.

Integrating DRP/MPS: DRP is used to carry out the material planning
necessary to support the needs of each DC. For retailers or wholesalers,
DRP will communicate to the buyers what they need to buy and when.
For manufacturers, DRP will generate the total distribution demand to
be input to the master production schedule (MPS).

The information regarding master production scheduling provided
earlier in the Quick-Slice MRP section applies to DRP, with one important distinction. DRP provides planning data to the sales & operations
planning function in addition to the master scheduling function. DRP
takes the sales forecasts and inventory goals by DC and determines how
much needs to be produced and when. Therefore, it is critical to recog-

nize DRP's contribution to the sales & operations planning process in manufacturing as well as master scheduling.

For retailers, wholesalers, and distributors, DRP reports what and when products should be purchased. Ultimately, this will lead to formal supplier scheduling arrangements, with the elimination of hard-copy purchase orders, and often utilizing EDI[21] hookups. For Fail-Safe Mini-DRP to work, it is necessary to develop a simple way of communicating DRP's recommended orders (manual or otherwise), as well as DRP's feedback regarding which purchase orders have been created.

Transportation Planning and Scheduling: When appropriate, modes of transport, desired size, frequency of shipments, and distribution lead times need to be determined for the Fail-Safe products. This is necessary to test and verify that transportation planning and scheduling will work properly. In many instances, though, the output will be unusable because most companies ship multiple products at the same time, and products in the Fail-Safe program will only represent a small portion of the total volume that is required to be shipped.

Nevertheless, it is worthwhile to proceed and test the planning module, since valuable insights will result. For example, the results can form the basis for revising the company's transportation strategies and formalizing an important cost area. Thus, when enough products are eventually planned, significant benefits can be realized as the fine tuning proceeds.

DATA MANAGEMENT

The same data management considerations described in the Quick-Slice MRP section above apply to Fail-Safe Mini-DRP. Note that inventory record accuracy of 95 percent plus must be maintained for every DC that stocks the products selected for Fail-Safe Mini-DRP.

---

[21] Electronic Data Interchange is an electronic linking of the customer's and supplier's computer, so that schedules and other key information can be rapidly communicated.

PERFORMANCE MEASUREMENTS

If you are a retailer, wholesaler, or distributor, the following performance measurements apply:

- Purchasing/inventory planning performance $+/-2$ percent
- Supplier delivery performance 95-to 100 percent

If you are a manufacturer, the same performance measurements described in the Quick-Slice MRP section will apply to the Fail-Safe Mini-DRP section.

CONCLUSION

Fail-Safe Mini-DRP is the logistics counterpart of Quick-Slice MRP. Therefore, the same concluding comments can be made here as with Quick-Slice MRP: Fail-Safe Mini-DRP is clearly different from the traditional approach but offers true advantages. Already tried and proven, we believe it will become the most common and accepted method of implementing DRP in the near future. It is a major breakthrough.

This concludes our discussion of the three Fast-Track Implementation approaches: Breakthrough JIT, Quick-Slice MRP, and Fail-Safe Mini-DRP. Now let's turn our attention briefly to company-wide implementation.

Fail-Safe Mini-DRP Detailed Implementation Plan

The following pages list the detailed implementation plan for Fail-Safe Mini-DRP. This plan is a modified version of the DRP Detailed Implementation Plan, altered to eliminate tasks that would not be a part of a Mini-DRP implementation. For example, the large education program that would be part of a full implementation has been cut back to an education program for the project team charged with the responsibility for implementing Mini-DRP.

In other cases, the tasks remain the same, but the amount of work is significantly reduced because they happen only for the Mini-DRP items. For example, inventory record accuracy would still have to be attained, but only on the items in Mini-DRP. In fact, the implementation plan for Mini-DRP is not much smaller than the implementation plan for a company-wide DRP implementation. However, the work required to implement Mini-DRP is significantly less and the time required is only a few months.

There are a number of abbreviations used in the RESPONSIBLE

column of the detailed implementation plans. The table below shows these abbreviations and their meaning:

Dept.	Department
Distr.	Distribution
Engr.	Engineering (either Design or Manufacturing)
Exec.	Executive
Mgmt.	Management
Mgr.	Manager
MIS	Management Information Systems
P&IC	Production & Inventory Control
Suprvsn.	Supervision

Fail-Safe Mini-DRP
Proven Path Detailed Implementation Plan

TASK	RESPONSIBLE	COMMENTS
1. AUDIT/ASSESSMENT I	Top Mgmt. Middle Mgmt.	Assess the company's current situation. In most cases, this is done with the help of an outside consultant with Class A credentials.
2. FIRST-CUT EDUCATION	Top Mgmt. Middle Mgmt.	What is DRP, how does it work, why should a company commit to it? Top management should attend the DRP Top Management Course, key middle managers should attend the DRP Three-Day Course.
3. VISION STATEMENT	Top Mgmt. Middle Mgmt.	A short, concise document defining what we want to accomplish, and when it should be in place.
4. COST/BENEFIT	Top Mgmt. Middle Mgmt.	A quick listing of the costs and benefits as applied to the Mini-DRP items only.
5. PROJECT ORGANIZATION	Top Mgmt.	Create the appropriate management and operational teams.
A. Executive Steering Committee.	Top Mgmt.	Include designation of Executive Torchbearer. Schedule review meetings once a month.
B. Project Team.	Top Mgmt.	Team Leader should be at least 50 percent on the project. Other team members from 10 percent to 25 percent depending on their role.
C. Outside counsel.	Top Mgmt.	Outside consultant with Class A experience.
6. PERFORMANCE GOALS	Top Mgmt. Middle Mgmt.	Using the ABCD Checklist, agree on expected performance levels and measurements.
7. INITIAL EDUCATION	Team Leader	Provide the necessary understanding to the team members who will be designing and using the new tools.
A. Outside education for team members.	Team Leader	To be effective team members, these people need exposure at either the DRP Top Management Course or the DRP Three-Day Course.
B. Project Team video course.	Team Leader	A series of business meetings where the general principles are translated into the specifics of operation for your company (for the Mini-DRP items only). Acquire the DRP Video Library.

163

Fail-Safe Mini-DRP
Proven Path Detailed Implementation Plan

TASK	RESPONSIBLE	COMMENTS
8. SALES, LOGISTICS, AND MANUFACTURING PROCESSES	Top Mgmt. Middle Mgmt.	Develop a detailed statement of how these processes will operate following implementation (for the Mini-DRP items only). The Project Team series of business meetings (Task #7B above) generally provides most of the information needed for this task.
9. PLANNING AND CONTROL PROCESSES		
A. Sales & Operations Planning.	Top Mgmt.	Identification of the systems necessary for effective planning (Mini-DRP items only). Start for all products, not just Mini-DRP product(s). Format, policies, unit of measure, and family designations can be developed in the first few meetings and revised as needed thereafter.
B. Demand Management.	Sales Mgr.	Mini-DRP items only.
C. Master Scheduling (Production or Purchase).	Logistics Mgr.	Mini-DRP items only. In a company with manufacturing operations, the term Master Production Scheduling is used. In a distribution operation without manufacturing, the term Purchase Schedule or Master Purchase Schedule is used.
1. Develop a master scheduling policy.	Top Mgmt. Sales & Mktg. Logistics Mgr.	Should address the following: 1. Procedure for changing the master schedule (production or purchase). Who can request a change, how the proposed change is investigated, and who should approve it. 2. Periodic reviews of actual performance vs. the master schedule (production or purchase) with an emphasis on problem resolution.
D. Distribution Requirements Planning.	Logistics Mgr.	Mini-DRP items only.
E. Supplier Scheduling & Development.	Purchasing Mgr.	Slice items only, simple supplier schedules.

164

Fail-Safe Mini-DRP
Proven Path Detailed Implementation Plan

TASK	RESPONSIBLE	COMMENTS
10. DATA MANAGEMENT		These are the steps required to attain the necessary levels of data accuracy (Mini-DRP items only).
A. Inventory Record Accuracy.	Distr. Center Mgrs.	Objective is a minimum 95 percent inventory record accuracy (Mini-DRP items only).
1. Provide the tools for limited access and transaction recording.	Distr. Center Mgrs.	It may be necessary to physically isolate the Mini-DRP items. Transaction system must be simple and easy to use.
2. Implement control-group cycle counting.	Distr. Center Mgrs.	Used to find and fix the root causes of errors.
3. Inventory all Mini-DRP items.	Distr. Center Mgrs.	Done to bring the accuracy of all Mini-DRP items to 95 percent. May have to be done several times to keep the accuracy at least 95 percent if the root causes of the errors have not been corrected.
B. Structure the distribution network.	Logistics Mgr.	Load bills of distribution to represent the distribution network (Mini-DRP items only).
C. Item Data.	Logistics Mgr. Purchasing Mgr.	The objective is to have knowledgeable people verify this information (Mini-DRP items only).
1. Verify order policies.	Logistics Mgr. Purchasing Mgr.	Fix the obvious errors in order quantities, use remainder as is.
2. Verify lead times.	Logistics Mgr. Traffic Purchasing Mgr.	Use current lead times, fix the obvious errors.
3. Verify safety stock levels.	Logistics Mgr. Purchasing Mgr.	Applies to independent-demand items consistent with master schedule policy. For dependent-demand items restrict to special circumstances only.

Fail-Safe Mini-DRP
Proven Path Detailed Implementation Plan

TASK	RESPONSIBLE	COMMENTS
11. PROCESS IMPROVEMENT		If process improvements can be done quickly to make it easier to implement Mini-DRP, use the JIT/TQC Detailed Implementation Plan.
12. SOFTWARE	MIS Mgr.	Select and implement the software to support the Mini-DRP. This may be temporary software (like a PC software package) or the current software if it is already up and running.
A. Select software.	MIS Mgr. Logistics Mgr.	A quick evaluation is essential here. In the case of "temporary" software, this can be done with a minimum of evaluation.
1. Acquire *The Standard System* book.	MIS Mgr. Logistics Mgr.	Available from Oliver Wight Limited Publications, this book provides an explanation of what a typical software package should provide.
B. Implement necessary modules.	MIS Mgr.	This should be done with little, if any, interfacing of systems. Typical modules include: Inventory Transactions, Bills of Material, Master Scheduling (Production or Purchase), Distribution Requirements Planning.
13. PILOT AND CUTOVER	Team Members	Typically, there is no pilot in a Mini-DRP implementation. All the Mini-DRP items are brought up on the system at once. However, the following implementation steps for a pilot are still appropriate for the implementation of Mini-DRP.
A. Complete three pilots.	Team Members	Pilots are: 1. Computer pilot to test the software. 2. Conference room pilot to test procedures and people's understanding. 3. Live pilot (or, in this case, Mini-DRP) to test the new processes and verify they are working.

Fail-Safe Mini-DRP

Proven Path Detailed Implementation Plan

TASK	RESPONSIBLE	COMMENTS
14. PERFORMANCE MEASUREMENTS	Team Members	Compare actual results to the previously agreed-upon key measurements. Typical performance measurements include: 1. Production Plan (or Open To Buy) performance. 2. Master Schedule (Production or Purchase) performance. 3. Supplier Delivery performance.
15. AUDIT/ASSESSMENT II	Top Mgmt. Middle Mgmt.	Re-assess the company's situation. Is it now time to implement DRP across all items? What's next?
16. ONGOING EDUCATION		In the case of Mini-DRP, ongoing education typically means initial education for the next phase of implementation.

Company-Wide
Implementations

Even with the use of Fast-Track Implementation techniques, a substantial need remains for the more traditional company-wide approach to implementing MRP II and DRP. (JIT does not have a company-wide implementation route. Rather it's implemented via a continuing series of controlled pilots.)

There are several reasons why the company-wide implementation process will continue to be widely used:

1. In some industries, it's simply not practical to manage a small segment of the business with a different set of tools.

2. Companies that implement initially via a Fast-Track (Quick-Slice MRP or Fail-Safe Mini-DRP) will at some point need to cut over to a company-wide implementation approach. While their short-term objectives in Fast-Track Implementation are quick results and quick payback, a company's long-term goal needs to be full implementation of these superior tools with their attendant competitive advantage.

Once again the Proven Path applies. First, audit/assessment I will lead some companies to adopt a company-wide approach from the outset (see

169

paragraph 1 above). In other cases, audit/assessment II, following the implementation of one or several slices of MRP or DRP, will lead a company to adopt a company-wide approach for the balance of its product line. This would be followed by first-cut education for key employees who have not yet been through that process. The next steps would be preparation of the vision statement, the cost/benefit analysis, organization of the project team and steering committee, establishment of performance measures, etc.

The key point here is that the steps in the Proven Path are the same. The Proven Path approach applies equally to Fast-Track or company-wide implementation, and it applies equally to MRP II, JIT, and DRP.

For additional information on company-wide implementations, please see:

MRP II: Making It Happen, Thomas F. Wallace, 1985, Oliver Wight Limited Publications, Inc., Essex Junction, VT.

Distribution Resource Planning, Andre J. Martin, 1983, Oliver Wight Limited Publications, Inc., Essex Junction, VT.

Summary

Faced with ever-growing competitive pressure, companies must improve or risk losing profit, market share, or even the entire business. In industry, this challenge has broadened from local to national, and now to global magnitude. The pressure is great, but so are the opportunities.

We at the Oliver Wight Companies believe the Proven Path responds to this need by providing its users with versatile new tools. The key aspects of the change to the Proven Path are integration and responsiveness:

Integration relates to the fact that we can no longer afford to pick a single approach. Complementary programs are needed for breakthrough results. Competition requires us to combine the powers of all programs by using an integrated approach.

Responsiveness is the new frontier of competition. Consequently, the Proven Path's Fast-Track Implementation approaches can help even those companies with the most urgent needs.

We hope this document provides a concise, understandable review of both the process and benefits of the Proven Path. Our objective at the Oliver Wight Companies continues to be focused on helping companies excel. We believe the Proven Path enables companies to achieve that objective by guiding them along the process of managing change.

The Original Proven Path[22]

The Proven Path consists of eleven steps. They are:

1. *First-Cut Education.* A handful of executives and operating managers from within the company must learn about MRP II before they can do a proper job of Step 2 (Cost Justification and Commitment).

2. *Cost Justification and Commitment.* The principle here is "Don't buy a pig in a poke." After these key executives and managers have learned about MRP II in first-cut education, they should put pencil to paper and calculate the expected costs and benefits. If the benefits, both tangible and intangible, don't justify the costs, the company should stop there, and not spend any more money on MRP II. If the numbers are compelling and all of the key people believe them, then they can make a commitment to doing it right.

3. *User-Controlled Project Team.* To succeed, each element of MRP II must be implemented by the same people who will be held accountable for operating it after it goes on the air. The project team is made up primarily of users, and is responsible for implementing MRP II at the operational level in the company.

4. *Full-Time Project Leader.* At least one key person from within the company should be freed from all other responsibilities to manage the implementation effort. There needs to be at least one person within the company for whom MRP II is priority number one. A part-time project leader will very often have to give preference to operational respon-

[22] Excerpted from *MRP II: Making It Happen* by Thomas F. Wallace.

sibilities at the expense of working on MRP II. This will cause the project to slow down and will decrease the odds for success.

5. *Executive Steering Committee.* To ensure success, top management must provide high-level leadership and must carry overall accountability for results. "The buck stops here." The steering committee is the means by which the general manager and his staff lead the entire implementation process. Without frequent top management reviews of progress, the project will tend to drift, and the odds for success will drop.

6. *Professional Guidance.* MRP II is not an extension of past experience. It's a whole new way of running a company. Companies implementing MRP II need periodic access to someone who has "been there"—someone who has been deeply involved in one or more Class A implementations—to serve as a catalyst, a sounding board, a giver of advice, and, most important, as a "conscience" to top management.

7. *Education of the Critical Mass.* A minimum of 80 percent of all the people in the company need to receive education on MRP II prior to implementation, with the balance shortly thereafter. For MRP II to succeed, many things will have to change, including the way that many people do their jobs. People need to know what, why, and how these changes will affect them. People need to be led to see the need to do their jobs differently, and the benefits that will result.

8. *Pilot Approach to MPS/MRP.* Don't play "you bet your company." Prove that master production scheduling and material requirements planning are working satisfactorily on a pilot group, before cutting over all products and parts.

9. *Close the Loop.* Tie in the execution systems—shop floor control, vendor scheduling, etc.—into the planning system.

10. *Finance and simulation.* Integrate the operational systems with the financial systems. Begin to use the "what if" capability.

11. *Dedication to Continuing Improvement.* Once a company reaches Class A, it has to keep working hard at making it better and better. It can then begin to use its Class A system as the "launch pad" for further progress.

The Proven Path is a logical, straightforward implementation approach, based completely on demonstrated results. As stated earlier, it is a lot of work but virtually no risk. If a company follows the Proven Path faithfully, sincerely, and vigorously, it will become Class A—and within two years.

PROVEN PATH

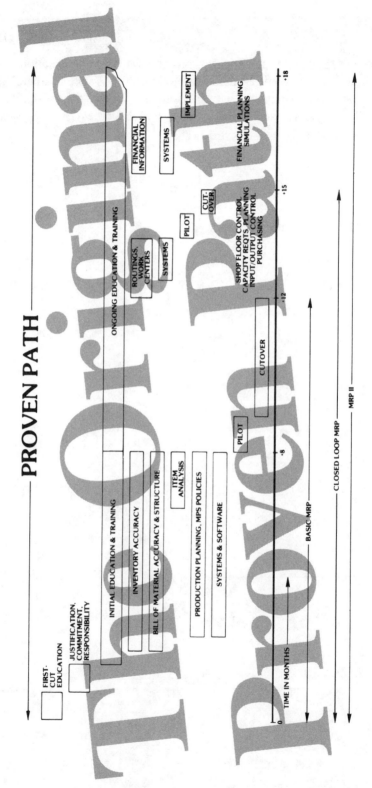

FIRST-
CUT
EDUCATION

JUSTIFICATION,
COMMITMENT,
RESPONSIBILITY

INITIAL EDUCATION & TRAINING

INVENTORY ACCURACY

BILL OF MATERIAL ACCURACY & STRUCTURE

ITEM ANALYSIS

PRODUCTION PLANNING, MPS POLICIES

SYSTEMS & SOFTWARE

PILOT

CUTOVER

ONGOING EDUCATION & TRAINING

ROUTINGS, WORK CENTERS

SYSTEMS

PILOT

CUT-OVER

FINANCIAL INFORMATION

SYSTEMS

IMPLEMENT

SHOP FLOOR CONTROL
CAPACITY REQTS. PLANNING
INPUT/OUTPUT CONTROL
PURCHASING

FINANCIAL PLANNING
SIMULATIONS

TIME IN MONTHS

0   •8   •12   •15   •18

BASIC MRP

CLOSED LOOP MRP

MRP II

Sample Implementation Plan

Sample Tailored Implementation Plan

TASK	RESPONSIBLE	COMMENTS
1. AUDIT/ASSESSMENT I	Top Mgmt. Middle Mgmt.	Assess the company's current situation. In most cases, this is done with the help of an outside consultant with Class A credentials.
2. FIRST-CUT EDUCATION	Top Mgmt. Middle Mgmt.	What is MRP II, how does it work, why should a company commit to it? Top management should attend the Top Management Course, key middle managers should attend the Five-Day Course, Executive Torchbearer and Team Leader should attend Successful Implementation Course.
3. VISION STATEMENT	Top Mgmt.	A short, concise document defining what we want to accomplish, and when it should be in place.

TASK	RESPONSIBLE	SCHEDULED START	DUE	ACTUAL START	DUE
1. AUDIT/ASSESSMENT I	L. Webb	2/14/XX	3/1/XX	2/14/XX	2/27/XX
		Audit completed, reviewed by top management group. Copies available for all managers.			
2. FIRST-CUT EDUCATION	J. Smith N. Duncan	3/1/XX	4/1/XX	3/2/XX	3/24/XX
		First-cut education included general manager and staff, factory superintendent, materials manager, purchasing manager.			
3. VISION STATEMENT	C. Peck	4/1/XX	4/5/XX	4/1/XX	4/10/XX
		Written by top management, posted in lobby, and distributed to all employees.			